D0387311

THROW THE LONG BOMB!

Authorized Edition

By JACK LAFLIN

with a foreword by
BART STARR

Illustrated by
GEORGE BARTELL

WHITMAN PUBLISHING COMPANY • Racine, Wisconsin

To Virginia,
who, along with millions of other
American wives, was forced to learn
pro football in self-defense.

J. L.

Copyright © 1967, by WESTERN PUBLISHING COMPANY, INC. Printed in U.S.A. All names, characters, and events in this story are entirely fictitious.

CONTENTS

A FOREWORD

WHEN A WRITER asked the late General Douglas MacArthur several years ago if he still felt as strongly about competitive athletics as he did when he was Superintendent of the United States Military Academy at West Point, the General replied, in part, "The opinions I expressed at West Point on the infinite values of athletic competition have but intensified with the passage of time. It is a vital character builder, for it molds the youth of our country for their roles as custodians of the republic. Fathers and mothers who

5

would make their sons into men should have them play the game, for on the fields of friendly strife are sown the seeds which on other fields, in future days, will bear the fruits of victory."

This is one of the most eloquent appraisals of athletic competition that I have ever heard. Since I have competed in athletics for many years, I can genuinely appreciate what the General said. Clean, wholesome athletic competition affords a young person the greatest head start imaginable. He is exposed very early to the importance of developing a good attitude or outlook on life. He soon realizes that he receives from life only that which he puts into it.

The young athlete also experiences the joys of attaining worthwhile goals, after having shown himself willing to accept their challenges enthusiastically. He learns quickly that the price of success is hard work, practice, and patience, and that to be successful he must be well organized and thoroughly prepared. He becomes familiar with such words as *Desire* and *Dedication,* because he sees that such ingredients are necessary in his makeup if he is to succeed.

As he grows older he begins to understand why pride of performance should underlie every attempt, so that a winning effort is the least he will settle for. He learns to accept himself, and if he fails at least he fails while daring greatly. Profiting from his mistakes, he comes back more determinedly the next time.

As the young player learns to evaluate such points, he becomes aware that every member of his squad must possess these same qualities, and all must work toward a common team objective. Team success should always rank ahead of individual glory.

Though I may be biased in favor of athletics, I honestly feel that the preceding points are but a few of the leadership qualities which competitive athletics develop in a youngster. Whether these qualities take him into the world of professional athletics, as they do Ronnie Baxter, or into some very different field of action, they are essential to his development as a fine human being.

BART STARR

1 | *Training Camp*

RONNIE BAXTER, six feet two inches and 195 pounds of rookie quarterback, tore his eyes away from a black, three-ring, loose-leaf binder, the New York Giants' playbook, that lay open before him on the classroom desk. Nervously running a hand over blond, brush-cut hair, Ronnie stared around the crowded main lecture hall of Fairfield University. *How many?* he wondered. Sixty or seventy, maybe, both newcomer and veteran alike, were packed into the hall. This was July, a month of brutal heat and high humidity. By September, when the squad had been pared down to the league limit of forty, over a third would be gone. They would have fallen victim to the dreaded "Turk," that legendary, mythical figure who haunted pro football camps. His pointing finger would separate those

9

destined to stay and go on to glory from the luckless others slated for outright release, trades, and eventual obscurity.

New York's head coach, Wayne Draven, entered the long room with its banked rows of seats via a rear door.

At last, Ronnie thought, *this is it—the first official orientation talk, the start of my life as a professional. How different, how much tougher is it going to be,* he asked himself, *than college football at Tulsa University? Will I be able to make good, or will I wind up as one of the forgotten, nameless, faceless people who meet the "Turk" in a few weeks?*

Ronnie smiled wryly, recalling the immediate past. Why, there were as many people, almost, in this very hall as the entire population of the small Oklahoma town from which he hailed!

Still somewhat shy and apprehensive at meeting strangers, a quiet, respectful young man of twenty-two who said "sir" to nearly everyone older than he, Ronnie Baxter had allowed his deeds with a football to speak for him through three years of college action. As a senior he had been ranked second nationally in total-offense statistics, completing 165 passes out of 311 attempted for his air-minded coach Charley Tubbs. Ronnie had thrown for twenty-one touchdowns in nine games, and this, along with his running on rollouts and option plays, had given him more than 2,000 yards gained for the season. He had been the number one draft choice of the Giants of the NFL. Having always yearned to play for the tradition-laden Yankee Stadium tenants, he was quite pleased when he found out which team had drafted him. He had signed with the Giants, for what the press reported as "a medium-sized bonus." Then had come the month of waiting following his graduation, the long flight from Oklahoma to Connecticut, posing for innumerable pictures, undergoing (for him) the ordeal of answering questions into mikes held by radio and TV sportscasters.

Along with the rest of the rookies, Ronnie went through the process of checking into camp. He was issued full equipment (with the exception of shoes, since each player was expected to supply his own), a locker in the field house, mimeographed training rules with an attached list of fines for violations, and a room assignment with another rookie quarterback hopeful, a young Negro named Dan McComb, the Giants' seventh-round draft choice from Grambling College.

The preliminaries, at least, lay behind him, Ronnie assured himself as he watched Wayne Draven mount the steps of the stage and halt on the wooden podium.

11

He was flanked on both sides by his assistant coaches, the head trainer, the team physician, the public relations man, the equipment manager, and sundry other members of the official Giant family.

A man in his fifties—a lined, gray-haired veteran of a dozen National Football League campaigns with the Giants two and three decades before—Draven was notorious for surface gruffness and the low boiling point of his temper, particularly on the field. The Giants had fallen on evil days, finishing last and next-to-last in the Eastern Conference the past two years. It was no secret that Draven was on the spot this season; the newspapers had crucified him over the winter and spring, and rumblings had come from fans and front office alike.

The unfairness of the criticism never bothered an old NFL hand like Draven. He knew that all his accumulated wisdom could not prevent fumbles at critical times, a porous secondary pass defense, injuries to key line and backfield personnel, and the mistakes of rookies. Nor could he do much about aging stars and their diminishing skills. He realized that a year of decision lay close at hand, for him and the Giants, which kept his disposition at a level very close to that of a bear with a thorn in its paw.

In baseball cap, polo shirt, blue shorts, and tennis

sneakers, Draven glared the assemblage into uneasy silence; then he began to read a roster from a clipboard. He started with "Adams" and ended with "Zarilla." Draven's voice was hoarse and rasping, the result of continued shouting from the sidelines in several hundred league games and in literally thousands of practice sessions.

"Anybody whose name I didn't call? Okay. On behalf of my entire staff I welcome all of you to summer training camp. Let me say right at the outset that nothing here is going to be fun and games. If there's a man present who thinks so, he might just as well get up, pack his gear, and steal quietly away. Plenty of you have been stars in college, and you have the scrapbooks of press clippings to prove it. My advice to you is—forget about them, quick. You can't eat press clippings, and you sure don't win games in the National Football League with them.

"I want one basic fact established. On this July tenth, so far as I'm concerned, you're starting from scratch. Past records are out the window. The twentieth draft choice will have the same chance of making the club as the first, and vice versa. I don't care if you're a rookie from the deepest canebrakes in Louisiana, or an All-Pro choice the last five years. You've got to prove to me that you're good enough to be one of the final forty, and I don't consider myself the easiest character in the world to convince. I'm not out to win any popularity contests. The only thing I care about is the Eastern Conference title, and then the championship, and then the Super Bowl. When you stop to consider this team has won only nine games out of its last twenty-eight, that's a tough assignment. But nothing's impossible in sports—you know that.

"There are two main things I demand. One is no back talk. You do as you're told and keep your mouth shut when you feel like arguing, or out you go. The men you see on this platform"—Draven waved a hand behind him toward his staff— "represent a couple hundred years of combined coaching and playing savvy. When I, or they, tell you something, you had better believe it's so. Most of us were getting knocked around every Sunday on a pro football field before ninety percent of you were born. You're here to learn, and learn you will, I guarantee it.

"So much for that. The other point I emphasize is hustle. You'll run everywhere; then when your tongues are hanging out, you'll run some more. I may not wind up fielding the best squad in the NFL, but I do intend to have the best-conditioned. All the teams in our league are roughly equal in skill. Therefore winning or losing often rests on how good your stamina is—

14

how many times you can feel you've arrived at the end of your rope physically and then reach down to find that little extra something that pulls a game out of the fire in the last two minutes.

"Now. I want you to open your playbooks to the first page. You'll see a mimeographed sheet, right on top, with the training rules listed, as well as a schedule of fines for breaking them and other club rules. I call your attention to the first figure you see."

Draven allowed a moment or two for the murmurs and the softly whistled "Whews!" to die down, then resumed.

"You're absolutely correct. We've listed the stiffest penalty first. Five double-o is the figure. Five hundred bucks for losing a playbook. This is mandatory—no excuses accepted, no return of the money after the season. Why? Because everything we're going to do all year is in there, that's why."

Draven's rasping voice droned on as he explained other fines: for missing meals, reporting late to practices or film sessions, breaking curfew, criticizing front-office policy to newspaper or radio or TV people. These infractions, Ronnie Baxter noted, ranged between twenty-five and one hundred dollars apiece.

"I don't want to take your money, men, but don't think I won't if necessary," Wayne Draven said.

The coach paused to light a cigarette, then blew out a long tendril of smoke. "So far as training is concerned, we operate on the principle that you're all mature adults, whether rookie or veteran. You should know how to handle yourselves. *And* take care of yourselves, too. We've got too much ground to cover in the next eight weeks to lead any of you around by the hand. Furthermore, I don't have to remind you that moderation is the keynote. Nobody had better forget it and expect to make this ball club."

Ronnie smiled. Draven's last remarks, he felt certain, didn't apply to him. He supposed the high regard he had for keeping in shape all year long, caring for his flat, muscular, rock-hard body, was a heritage from his beloved father, a gym and physical education teacher at the district high school Ronnie had attended back home. At the age of fifty, the elder Baxter could still run five miles, play a full basketball game, or gambol for an hour on the parallel bars without even drawing a labored breath.

Draven shuffled some sheets of paper on the lectern and held one up.

"This will be posted on the bulletin board later, but so you'll all be familiar with it now I'm going to outline our daily schedule. You'll soon find that sacktime commandos are in deep trouble." He waited for the ripple of laughter that arose to subside, then went on.

"The only time you'll really be able to call your own is when you're sleeping. The rest of it is ours. You veterans know all this by heart. What's coming is for the benefit of the rookies. They're expecting things to be run like a military camp, and they won't be too far wrong. Here goes.

"Seven A.M. is reveille. Seven fifteen to seven forty-five, breakfast served in the Freshman Commons. It's the big building with the Gothic spires a hundred and fifty yards or so from Campion Hall, which is the name of the dormitory you're quartered in. You'll get fruit juice, fresh fruit, hot or cold cereal, bacon or ham or sausages and eggs, coffee or tea.

"From eight to nine thirty, study and learn play assignments from your books. At nine forty-five sharp, on the field for calisthenics, wind sprints, dummy scrimmage, general sharpening of plays. Quarterbacks, running backs, flankers, and ends will meet in one group; offensive linemen in another; defensive linemen in a third; linebackers and defensive backs in a fourth, with the appropriate coaches concerned in charge. As the day wears on, these groups will gradually merge until the full squad is working together.

"At noon we knock off for lunch. It'll be light but

17

hearty—cold cuts, hamburgers, sandwiches, soup, iced tea, and so forth.

"Afternoon sessions begin promptly at two and run until four thirty. At times we'll hold special meetings for backs, linemen, ends, suicide squads, and defensive secondary. Wednesday afternoons you're off. You can go to the beach, play golf, take in a movie, or just drive around the Connecticut countryside.

"Dinner's at six. Sirloin steaks at least three times a week. Roast beef, chicken, and pot roast are the standbys. We gave up on lamb a couple of years ago. We found out you guys didn't like it. Whenever the chef put it on the menu, most of the squad started going 'Baaa, Baaa, Baaa.' I didn't know if this was a football camp, a sheep ranch, or a table down at Morey's in New Haven."

His heavy-handed attempts at humor were always effective in loosening up the first-day tightness, Draven had discovered. He was never quite sure whether the players chuckled because what he said was genuinely funny or merely from a sense of duty. In either case, his jokes served their purpose as icebreakers.

"At seven P.M., skull sessions, blackboard drills, spot quizzes on how well you're absorbing your play assignments, film sessions of previous exhibition games or scrimmages. Curfew hour for being back in your rooms

is eleven o'clock. I warn you, we'll check up once in a while. Lights out at eleven thirty, and that's your day. Are there any questions on what we've covered up till now?"

Hands shot up in various parts of the hall. The Giant head coach fielded the queries with a practiced ease born of the almost certain knowledge that the same ones would be asked year after year.

Following that, Draven introduced his assistants: Bert Diehl, offensive backfield; Hamlin Turner, ten years All-Pro, holder of the NFL record for pass interceptions, defensive backfield; Larry Masters, offensive ends; Mike O'Hargan, the bulky ex-Chicago Bear, defensive ends; Remmie Braun, all 300 pounds of him, defensive line; Al Bradshaw, offensive line. Draven would take the quarterbacks under his own wing. Each spoke briefly of his particular responsibility and how he intended to handle it.

The head trainer, Yogi Di Orio, a small, wizened man who couldn't have weighed more than 120 pounds soaking wet, appeared next. He detailed the importance of each player's reporting injuries promptly, however minor, so that they could be promptly attended to and thus not become major. He then outlined schedules for the taping of ankles on scrimmage and game days, with the added warning that such taping was compulsory by league rule and would result in a fine if not carried out. And finally the trainer explained the use of whirlpool baths and other therapeutic aids for the bruises and sprains that always occurred during the season.

The team physician, Dr. Melvin Lotts, held forth for fifteen minutes on the medical aspects of pro football, dwelling on some of the most common ailments the players would be prone to, such as pulled hamstring muscles, sprained ankles, twisted knees, bruised shins, hip pointers. In support of Wayne Draven's earlier statements, Dr. Lotts confirmed that superb conditioning did much to cut down on the serious types of injuries that could sideline a player for weeks or perhaps the entire season.

There was a great deal more. When the meeting finally broke up, Ronnie Baxter was surprised, looking at his watch, to find that two and a half hours had elapsed.

He spent the remainder of that first day getting acquainted and trying to equate names with faces. Occasionally he flashed a happy smile when he ran into someone against whom he had played in college. Although it required some time, the young quarterback began to lose some of his basic shyness when thrown into the company of new people, even though they might be rookies like himself. There were seventeen of them in the camp; eventually Ronnie came to know them quite well.

The veterans, as Ronnie had anticipated, were another matter entirely. They were polite and externally friendly, yet maintained a certain aloofness that left no doubt concerning the status they enjoyed. Their attitude was clear. Each year talented new men arrived who represented a challenge to the veterans' job security. Was a man supposed to assist and encourage another who was trying his best to shove him onto the bench? If it happened, so be it. But the veterans were simply not eager to help forge the instruments of their own destruction, which was to be expected. A line between the two groups was drawn early and remained throughout the training period.

Later that evening Ronnie voiced some of his nagging doubts and uncertainties to his roommate, Dan McComb.

"I wonder what it'll be like tomorrow, Dan. How do you think it'll go? Being out on the practice field, I mean, with all those veteran stars. Arnie Jennings, "Horse" Collins, Frank Morris, Ed Pell, all the rest of them. Can a guy help but be a little scared the first time he puts on cleats with a crew like that?"

McComb had a slow southern accent and a realistic

outlook. He folded his hands behind his head and said, "None of them worries me any, Ron. They aren't quarterbacks. Now, if you were talking about Chips Farrell, Harry Flood, Ben Barton, and yourself, then I'd start thinking. Five of us in camp, and maybe the team'll carry three, possibly only two, once the season starts. The odds aren't so hot in our particular group. But why fret over it, Ron? What will be, will be.

"Well, it's almost time for lights-out. I've got to get my beauty rest. See you bright and early."

A variety of emotions chased themselves through Ronnie Baxter's excited mind as he lay in the dark. Bonus rookies had come down the pike before, players paid far more than he had received, and they hadn't made the grade. What, exactly, were his chances of surviving the "Turk's" first visit, and his second, and his third? Would he be excessively nervous and perform badly from the beginning? Or would he catch on to the Giants' offensive system quickly?

Sleep arrived with maddening slowness for Ronnie. He reviewed the so-called bread-and-butter plays from his book: power leads, sweeps, counter traps, draws, screens, slant-in and sideline passes. Then his mind turned to the various defenses he could expect to see: basics, variations, shifting and stunting defenses, goal line gap 8's, and on top of them. . . .

Sometime before the early July sun started peeping in his window, Ronnie dreamed he had become the Giants' number one quarterback and had brilliantly led the team in his rookie year to an undefeated season.

Then came seven A.M. and an abrupt return to reality. Ronnie's life as a pro was about to begin.

2 | The Grind Begins

THAT SECOND day formed a pattern, lengthened into
a week, and somehow the week stretched into three.
For Ronnie Baxter, rookie quarterback, it was a period
of stress, strain, disillusionment, and the hardest mental and physical work he had ever known in his life.

There was one basic reason, he ruefully admitted.
Most of the skills he had acquired over four years of
college football had to be unlearned in the pro ranks,
or at least drastically changed. Although Ronnie was
normally eager and smart and quick to learn, the professional way of doing things, in some instances, came
to him with painful slowness.

The twenty-one days had been brutally difficult:
endless skull sessions, calisthenics, films, dummy scrimmages, drills, quizzes, a thousand isolated facts to be

25

committed to memory beyond any chance of forget-
ting.

Even in slumber Ronnie couldn't escape the sights
and sounds of the New York Giants' Fairfield training
camp. As he tossed and turned fitfully they all blended
into a single panorama of noisy, highly organized
chaos.

The five quarterbacks—Ronnie, Ben Barton, Dan
McComb, Harry Flood, and the holdover top man,
Chips Farrell—practicing alternately under the watchful eye of Wayne Draven. In the huddle. Call a play.
"Forty-four tackle trap, on two. Ready—break!"
Which, translated, meant a handoff to the number
four back, who would hit the number four line hole,
the play starting on the second count. Barking signals.
"Blue, even, set. Seventy-six, thirty-nine, twenty-one.
Hut! Hut!" A blur of motion as split end and flanker
perform their assigned tasks; tight end goes out to
block a phantom linebacker. The slap of leather as the
exchange is completed. Ronnie thinking the maneuver had been accomplished with crisp dispatch, only
to hear Draven screaming, "Stick it right in his belly,
Baxter. Don't wait. And get out of the path of the
action faster. You hang around near the line like that
and there's every excuse in the world for some defensive man coming through to belt you into next month,

whether you're rid of the ball or not. Run it again, and let's see you do it right this time!"

Pass patterns. They became nightmares to Ronnie. If the head coach found fault with his ball handling on running plays, he wound up positively apoplectic upon occasions when Ronnie put the ball into the air.

Once, in the huddle, Ronnie called for a zone flood pattern left, in which the flanker moved into the slot inside the split end; at the snap both they and the running back would move at various depths into a given defensive zone. After the third "Hut!" Ronnie dropped straight back to his imaginary pass protection pocket, pump-faked to the right, moved two steps left, hesitated a half second, and rifled the ball deep downfield to the split end, Arnie Jennings.

Draven wasn't impressed by the beautiful 50-yard spiral Ronnie had thrown, nor with the catch, nor with Jennings' moves and speed. Instead he blew his whistle, bawled "Hold it!" and glared at Ronnie.

Draven brandished a stopwatch. "All right, Baxter, read the time off for me."

"Four and two-tenths seconds, Coach."

"Exactly. So tell me what I'm yelling about."

"I was too slow getting the pass away."

"You'd better believe it. Up here in the NFL you have a maximum of three and a half seconds to get rid of that ball or you're a dead man. I prefer you to aim for three seconds flat. With every extra tick of the watch, there's also an increased chance for an ineligible receiver to drift downfield. So even if you complete it, we'll wind up with a fifteen-yard penalty. One other thing. Don't dance out of that pocket! You're not Frank Packenham of the Vikings! I don't like scrambling quarterbacks. They get killed too easily. As far as I'm concerned, the only time I ever want to see a quarterback running out of the pocket is from sheer fright! Got it? Okay. Again. Do it right now!"

To Ronnie Baxter, it seemed as if he "did it right" at least several hundred times a day.

Of all the squad members, Ronnie had to give the linemen the most credit. If he felt occasionally that his own lot was tough, he was forced to admit one must really love the game of football to undergo what they did. Off to the side in a sweating group, toiling nearly unnoticed except by Remmie Braun and Al Bradshaw, they cheerfully submitted to a multitude of torturous drills designed to strengthen leg and shoulder muscles, improve initial charges, and help them wade through determined pass blockers to chop down an opposing quarterback.

There was the "Road Map," for instance, and Ronnie winced whenever he thought about it. A huge, seven-man blocking sled with padded pieces protruding at waist level, it was supposed to quicken the reflexes of the 250- to 290-pound linemen, who were not exactly whippets to begin with. Four beefy tackle candidates might take three-point stances simultaneously, and then Braun's commands would ring out in rapid, staccato succession: "Hit it! Right! Left! Right! Half round! Jigger! Hit the ground! Up! Jigger! Half round! Hit it again! Peel off! Pursue right! Okay, next four!" If any foolhardy player had arrived in camp out of condition, the "Road Map" drill quickly separated him from those in shape.

One of Al Bradshaw's fiendish inventions was the "Nutcracker." Bradshaw had devised the exercise, as he put it, "to determine right quick who likes to knock heads and who doesn't." Inside a narrow lane delineated by two tackling dummies, a ball carrier ran full speed behind a blocker, while a potential tackler tried to penetrate the interference and pulverize the ball carrier. It was the most primitive, one-on-one, man-against-man situation imaginable—but highly effective. An hour of the "Nutcracker" in ninety-degree temperatures was enough to make even the strongest lineman flinch.

Actually Ronnie little doubted who in the Fairfield camp deserved that "strongest" title. It fell without too much competition to Jim Karnarveron, nicknamed "Buddha" by his teammates because of his great size and girth. At six-eight and 290, the Giants' left defensive tackle possessed muscles on top of muscles. One morning while taking out his natural hostility for opposing linemen on a blocking dummy known as Lollipop, Karnarveron shattered the thick spring on the device, cracking it top and bottom, a feat never before accomplished. Word, as it often did, soon got around. For several days thereafter, knots of gaping, curious spectators gathered in the area to inspect the spring.

In addition, the long-suffering and underpublicized linemen grunted and groaned over a variety of other blocking and tackling contraptions with such colorful names as "Big John," "Ramback," "Springback," and "Guideback."

Linebackers and secondary defenders came in for their share of hard, grueling labor. Man-for-man and double-team pass coverage, interception drills, blitzes, keys, switching, calling out offensive sets, zone defense, a thousand finer points that the defensive backfield must be sharp on, and all were worked over day after day, reworked, and then, inevitably, "done again right." Hamlin Turner was in overall charge of this phase. His tongue could be as caustic as Wayne

Draven's. No one was exempt, yet no one seemed to mind. All these men were professional athletes, with the skill and knowledge that accompanied the term. When they fouled up a defensive situation or allowed a wide receiver to fake them out of their shoes, they expected a rebuke, nor were they disappointed. As a matter of strict fact, Ronnie observed, it appeared that Turner zeroed in particularly on the veterans, probably figuring that with their longer experience they should make fewer mistakes.

Hal Honegger, a five-year man at right safety, received a typical blast from Turner after a rookie flanker had muscled past him for a pass catch on a combination of head fake and sheer power: "Why did you move that way? Two more steps and you could have forced him out of bounds! Never move that way or they'll have you riding the bench before the season's two games old!" Then he turned on cornerback Gunner Swenson, beaten badly by Arnie Jennings, who had gotten behind him for an over-the-shoulder catch: "No, no, no, and again NO! You've got to move *through* the ball, *through* the ball. Don't let it come to you, move *through* it!" Turner's voice, unamplified, rose to a shriek that easily competed with Draven's built-in bullhorn.

Bobo Zarilla, the team's place-kicker, and Les Tremont, the punter, practiced by themselves at one end of the field. Zarilla would methodically start booting from the 25, kick ten from there, move back to the 30, kick ten more, and so on out to the midfield stripe. Then he would return downfield, five yards at a clip, until he reached the original starting point. Whole hordes of local kids did the retrieving, bringing back the kicked footballs in relays.

Les Tremont, who had led all NFL punters the preceding season with a 46.5 average, belted high, booming floaters up into the cloudless July sky. Occasionally he would shake his head in annoyance when a clinker flew off the side of his foot and bounced to earth 30 or so yards away.

Finally there were the ever-present fans, mostly men, although a few women dropped around, too, who swarmed in droves around the camp. The concentration was especially heavy on weekends. They sat sometimes several thousand strong in the wooden bleachers. They pestered players for autographs and photographs and good-naturedly ducked when a pass receiver or ball carrier, complete with blockers in front, came boiling over the sidelines to end in a tangled heap on the grass.

All the visual and aural evidences of his first pro football training camp swarmed over Ronnie; live to be a hundred, make the last cut or not, he knew they would be indelibly stamped on his mind.

With the passage of time, Ronnie gradually realized how much greater were the pressures on Wayne Draven than on himself—a mere first-year man trying to stay on the squad. On a certain afternoon Ronnie was approached by a writer. Seeking the eternal "fresh angle" for a column, the scribe wanted to know what Ronnie thought of Wayne Draven.

"Well, sir," Ronnie said slowly, the words coming out in labored groups as he groped for just the right ones, "he can make you wish you could find a hole, crawl in it, and pull it in after you. If you foul up, he gets under your skin pretty well. But you can't blame him. He's got a job to do—to make pros out of us. That could be a mite hard on anyone's disposition." Ronnie finished with a shy grin.

The newspaperman walked away, apparently satisfied. Ronnie was relieved. Even after his feats during his senior year at Tulsa, when he had appeared on numerous radio and television shows and submitted to dozens of searching interviews, he still considered himself basically a small-town boy thrust suddenly into a big-town setting. He wondered if the vague unease he always experienced around newspapermen would ever completely leave him.

During the first week of practice the "Turk" had visited Fairfield, and the squad had been trimmed to a more workable size. A number of men had left, among them Dan McComb, Ronnie's roommate. McComb had left with no regrets; in fact, he had seemed quite casual about the whole process.

"Doesn't really matter that much, Ron," Dan had said with a shrug as he packed his gear. "It isn't the end of the world. There's always the chance another team will pick me up. I'll call around. If nobody wants me, I can go back to college in the fall and start again where I left off. I still have two semesters to complete for my degree in engineering. Might as well learn early rather than late whether I can play pro ball. Right now it looks as though I can't. Take it easy, Ron. Give 'em you-know-what. I'll see you soon, I hope."

Somewhat to his surprise, Ronnie had survived the initial application of the ax. His anxious concern over his fate had reached a peak toward the end of that first week as the bad news reached the others. Despite his bonus status and his selection as a number one draft choice, Ronnie's retention by the Giants left him shaken and more than a trifle astonished. The rookie quarterback, if the truth be known, had an extremely overdeveloped sense of his own shortcomings. He thought he had made an inexcusably poor showing.

Some of it he attributed to nervousness, some to mere mechanical errors.

Whatever the reason, breathing a silent prayer of thanks that he had been spared, he vowed to apply himself harder in the future; he would study his playbook day and night, during meals—whenever he had an uncluttered moment of any kind. He knew that learning the intricacies of over a hundred basic plays and variations from a variety of sets and formations was not going to be a picnic. Pro left. Pro right. I formation. Slot to either side, or both. Double wing. Man in motion. Zone flood, or triple flanker left and right, and so on down the line through the two-inch-thick, two-pound playbook. Would he ever get them all straight in his tired brain?

On the Friday before the Sunday of the Giants' first preseason game at Ithaca, New York, against the Pittsburgh Steelers, another cut cropped up. The squad was now down to fifty. Ronnie was still on it.

He celebrated by writing a long letter to his parents and another to his college football coach, then taking in a movie in nearby Bridgeport. For Ronnie Baxter it was a rare and welcome night of relaxation.

3 | *Baptism by Fire*

As THE GIANTS' charter plane droned through blazing hot sunlight nine thousand feet over New York State, Ronnie Baxter relaxed in his seat, eyes half-closed. Shifting his gaze from side to side, he observed his teammates busying themselves at sundry pastimes.

Arnie Jennings, the rangy split end, studied his playbook while Frank Morris, who manned the tight post at the opposite end of the line, dozed next to him. Chips Farrell and Harry Flood, holdover quarterbacks from the preceding season, had their heads together across the aisle. Andy Robertson and Jim Karnarveron, two members of the front defensive four, snored gently just in front of Ronnie, despite the racketing clamor of the aircraft's engines. (It was jokingly said of Robertson that he was a direct descendant of Rip Van

Winkle and could easily sleep atop a barbed-wire fence.) Wayne Draven held court in the forward section, outlining plays with the usual diagrams of x's, o's, and arrows attached to wiggly lines, for the assistant coaches. Various others, known for their notable lack of enthusiasm about flying, stared stonily straight ahead, read magazines, or argued noisily over a gin rummy game.

Taking stock, Ronnie reviewed the kaleidoscopic events of the past few weeks. While he couldn't help feeling at times that the powers that be were minimizing the good things he did and accentuating his numerous rookie errors, Ronnie was also of the opinion he was making definite progress. That he had survived this far was sufficient proof, he thought.

Wayne Draven's caustic manner and acid-dipped tongue seemed somewhat overdone to Ronnie. The young quarterback had not often been exposed to such explosiveness of temper; he was more accustomed to the quiet authority of his father, who maintained discipline with a look or a wink and seldom raised his voice. Even in high school and college Ronnie's coaches had been older, more soft-spoken men, persuaders rather than drivers.

However, Ronnie had recently become aware of one extremely valuable fact: Attention by the coaches,

Draven especially, could be a useful indicator of how a rookie was getting along. When the staff ceased yelling or flinging suggestions it usually meant they simply were no longer interested in a particular player. When that occurred, the unfortunate individual might soon expect to hear the "Midnight Footsteps," the equivalent of receiving a visit from the "Turk."

Ronnie also guessed he was still more than a little awed by the entire scene. He was tremendously impressed by the easy camaraderie of the veterans, their expensive clothes, their relaxed manner of talking to the writers who traveled with the club—all the things that showed the world that they were "old pros."

To choose an example at random, there was Willie Collins, the 235-pound fullback whose number 32 had galloped around NFL gridirons for six seasons now. Off the field, Collins had been dubbed "Horse" (shortened from "Clothes Horse") by the rest of the squad, a natural nickname considering the extent of his wardrobe. Ronnie felt sure a large part of the former Maryland ace's salary must go to the tailors, since he never seemed to wear the same outfit two days running. Ties and either sports jackets or suits were a club rule on road trips, which was right up Collins' alley. Reflecting on the meager contents of his own closet, Ronnie Baxter marveled when the elegantly dressed fullback

39

pranced up the aisle on his way forward.

Ronnie listened to the throbbing of the engines, noticed the changed slant of the sunlight as they made a sweeping, half-speed starboard turn. There came the grinding, jarring sound of the landing gear being lowered and locked into place. The FASTEN SEAT BELTS sign appeared. Soon the Giants would be landing at Thompson County Airport, which served the Ithaca area.

"The 'Turk,' " Ronnie breathed. "He's been at Fairfield several times already, and he isn't through yet. What's the squad down to? Fifty, a bit less?" The pre-season schedule, starting the next day, would prune several more. Injuries would take their toll, although they could be considered a two-edged sword—knocking some out of a chance they had struggled hard for, affording others a stay of execution, since many candidates at one position might be struck down simultaneously. Actually, barring the leveling influence of twisted ankles or pulled muscles, what chance did a rookie have of making the club? "Especially," mused Ronnie as an afterthought, "a rookie quarterback?"

Life was hard for the first-year men in a pro camp, without question. It was not as difficult as it had been, say, twenty years earlier; it was still a situation in which certain basic facts were thrust home with sudden and dramatic swiftness. Veterans and rookies were housed, quartered, and fed in a single large body, attended joint classroom sessions, and practiced together. Nevertheless, there remained a subtle barrier between the two groups that grew ever wider as the days and weeks of preseason training passed.

Ronnie Baxter recalled with a smile some of the mild hazing involved—the lunches in the mess hall, when the rookies followed the age-old custom of standing on their chairs, hands over hearts, and bellowing out their college alma mater songs for the amused benefit of the entire assemblage. It was a small thing, of course, but it emphasized a very tangible line, one that could only be erased completely by superhuman mental and physical effort plus superior performance on the field.

Amid the savage, ceaseless warfare of professional football, the comings and goings, the jockeying for position, and the competition for open roster spots, Ronnie was happy to note that race relations were uniformly excellent. Even those players who hailed from the Deep South were not likely to bring the matter up. Most refused to judge a fellow squad member on the basis of color, personality, or background. Generally, one criterion alone prevailed: Could a man cut the mustard when the opening whistle blew? If

41

he couldn't, he was out. It was just as simple as that.

The plane, flaps lowered and air speed reduced, circled preparatory to landing. Ronnie leaned forward in his seat, still wrapped in thought. High school and college ball had been tough, sure. Desire had to be present, along with determination and self-control. Even so, there was never the all-pervasive intensity, the urge, the driving need for success and perfection on the playing field that characterized the pro game.

Limbering up on the sidelines alongside Ben Barton the next day, conscious of a warm trickle of sweat inching its way down between his shoulder blades directly underneath the big number 19 on the back of his jersey, Ronnie Baxter could feel the tension building up inside him like steam in a boiler. A full house had been predicted for this initial preseason contest involving the Giants and the Steelers. If the crowd already filing into Schoellkopf Field was any indication, it would indeed be.

Ronnie rifled short-range spirals to the split end, Arnie Jennings. The latter lobbed the ball back underhand; it was established procedure never to return a football hard to a quarterback, for fear of injury to his hand or fingers.

Peering about him, Ronnie's interested gaze took

in the clubhouse to his left, with the yellow brick facade of Teagle Hall behind it. Then, turning to his right, he saw the temporary bleachers in the end zone, where the scoreboard clock perched, storklike, on long metal legs, and a seething mass of humanity fitting itself into the half-ovals of the east and west stands. Ronnie experienced a great thrill of pride and achievement. He might, he thought, be standing amid the academic influences of an Ivy League campus, yet he was about to embark on his very first game of professional football in the red, white, blue, and silver livery of the New York Giants!

"How you feeling, Ronnie?" Barton asked him.

Baxter laughed, although the sound had a brittle, false ring to it. "Calm, Ben. Calm. Can't you tell?" Ronnie held out a hand and pretended it was shaking. For a brief instant he wondered how much of the act was pretense. He had known butterflies before, but none so violent as these.

Ben Barton threw the ball to Jennings. "Me, too," Ben said. "No sweat. Just another game. Ha! Who am I trying to kid?"

At last the preliminaries were over. The officials met in the center of the field and indicated who had won the toss. Chips Farrell represented the offense, Ron Lewis the defense, for the Giants. They would be game captains. Both squads huddled briefly around their coaches, two sets of yells split the muggy, sticky August air, and the fans settled back expectantly to await the kickoff.

Starting from their own 17, the Giants had the ball. Ed Pell, from his halfback slot, gained a couple of yards over right guard. Horse Collins, the fullback, had nowhere to go on the next play as the opposing middle linebacker, keying on him, fired through to nail his man for a yard loss.

On third and 9, Farrell followed the part of Wayne Draven's game plan which called for early exploitation of Marty Faust, a rookie playing at weak-side cornerback. The Giant quarterback sent Arnie Jennings, his split end, deep on what was essentially a Z-out pattern. Jennings' quick, deft fake left a bewildered Faust in his wake as Farrell laid the leather in Jennings' arms on the Steelers' 48. Before he was finally hauled down at the 10, Arnie had gained 72 yards!

Two plays later Collins bulled his way over from 7 yards out, behind the crisp blocking of Don Payson and Booker T. Bellson, left tackle and guard respectively. Bobo Zarilla's kick upped the count to 7–0, Giants, with a little more than two minutes gone in the opening period.

Relaying instructions from the press box to the bench on the telephone headset, Ronnie Baxter excitedly watched the kicking team deploy, and the Steelers' deep men trot toward their goalposts. Farrell, he thought, had made it look so absurdly simple! And Jennings' pass pattern—what great moves the man had! Ronnie itched for action, though he knew he wasn't slated to play until the second half started.

Ronnie's face grew longer and longer while the remaining minutes of the first half unfolded. Following their initial burst of 83 yards in five plays, the Giants could do nothing right and the opposition nothing wrong. The offense was a nightmare of dropped passes, missed blocking assignments, inept pass protection, and costly fumbles. Four times the Giants erred when they had the ball; on each occasion the alert Pittsburgh Steelers turned the mistakes into points on the scoreboard. Although the Giants penetrated deep enough in the second quarter for Bobo Zarilla to kick long-range field goals of 38 and 44 yards, the New Yorkers entered the dressing room at the intermission trailing 24 to 13.

Scuffling angrily along the worn concrete in front of the blackboard, tie askew, jacket flapping, Wayne Draven confronted his charges. The sound of band music from the field filtered in through the open windows. Draven turned on them, face dark, eyes angry.

"I realize this is only the first preseason game," Draven fumed, "but there's still no reason why you should look as lousy as you did out there. You were miserable! *Miserable,* I tell you. We've only got twenty minutes. Believe me, that wouldn't even begin to give me enough time to point out all the things that went wrong!

"Fumbles I can live with; they're part of football. Interceptions happen. The weather's hot, and even taking salt tablets you dehydrate fast. But the fundamentals! Or rather the lack of them! That I can't stand! Will you gentlemen kindly explain to me what we've been doing at Fairfield the past four weeks? Drilling on fundamentals! And now, for thirty full minutes, you seem to have forgotten every single one!"

Draven worked himself up to a fever pitch, citing chapter and verse. Blown assignments. Missed tackles. Wrong pass patterns. Slowness off the initial charge. Offsides. Illegal motion. Broken plays. Mixups on handling the ball. Then, through at last with the general, blanket indictment, Coach Draven went to specifics. Illustrating on the blackboard with quick chalk slashes the adjustments in both offense and defense he desired in the second half, Draven laid out an

46

overall plan of attack he considered might be the most effective to erase the Steelers' 11-point lead.

He looked at his watch. "Well, that's it, men," he said. "There's nothing more we can do in here. The rest is up to you once you hit the field. Ronnie Baxter'll open at quarterback and go as long as he's able."

Ronnie sat nervously on the hard wooden bench, palms moist, heart beating furiously, while Zarilla kicked off to the Steelers to start the third period. He edged forward in an agony of scarcely suppressed anxiety for the length of time it took the defensive unit to hold and force a punt. Then suddenly it was time to take the field. In his anxiety, Ronnie found his preparations for action slipping past him as if in a dream: lower helmet onto head with fumbling fingers; check chin strap; run onto the field with the offense group to find the ball at the Giants' 21; listen to the roar from 25,000 people assault his eardrums with what seemed like a great deal more violence than many larger crowds he had played before at Tulsa.

The other ten men folded in around him as he called his first play. Ronnie stared at their toes, a trick he had learned years before to aid his concentration. It was a simple hand-off to Ed Pell. He slapped the ball into the running back's belly and stepped nimbly out of the way. Pell gained a hard-fought 2 yards.

"The linebackers were coming in on that last one," Jack Strawbridge, the right tackle, observed as he came back to the huddle. "We had a hard time getting blocking angles with all the stunting they were doing just before the snap."

"I noticed that," agreed Ronnie. "The middle looked wide open. The quick slant-in should go." He gave the number of the play, that of the tight end, Frank Morris, and the snap count, two.

As the lines converged, Ronnie had a split second to recognize that this time the rush came from the four Steeler front men. In addition, Morris didn't get an immediate release, being held up and belted by one defensive end. Hoping to fire his pass to where Morris should have been after his late start, Ronnie tried to thread the needle past the upflung arms of an onrushing lineman. He didn't quite succeed. Deflected, the ball wobbled feebly in the air behind Morris, then was picked off by a linebacker. Before he was hurled to the ground and had the breath driven from him by 275 pounds of defensive tackle, Ronnie heard the concerted yell from 25,000 throats that meant the pass had been intercepted. Frank Morris, the intended receiver, hauled down the ball carrier, but the Steelers were knocking on the door again at the Giant 30.

Still tense and tight and, above all, angry with him-

self, Ronnie knelt beside Wayne Draven.

"It was a good call, Ron," Draven said grudgingly. "Except for one thing. You've got to learn when to eat the football for a short loss and when to throw it. That was one time you should have eaten it."

In six plays the Steelers took the ball in. They chewed up the final 11 yards on a post-pattern pass from quarterback Bill Neilson to his flanker, Jeff Darnley. When the extra-point kick rocketed out of sight over the top of the clubhouse roof, the Giants trailed by 18 at 31–13.

Watching the Steeler kickoff sail down to Hal Honegger on the Giants 1-yard line, Draven stood with an arm around Ronnie's shoulder pads and barked terse instructions.

"Okay, you're going right back in," he growled. "They'll be expecting us to put the ball in the air immediately, playing catch-up football, especially since we never have established much of a running game. Keep them honest and try to cut down on the red-dogging some. Run the ball the first series: counter trap, off the fake pitch; power sweep; draw. Muscle hasn't worked very well, so maybe a little finesse will. If you make a first down in good field position, open up. Throw that long bomb."

Ronnie felt his coach's smack on the rump as he

trotted onto the field with the rest of the offensive unit. Honegger had made a good runback down the sideline, so the Giants were in business on their own 39.

Encouraged, a few of the butterflies out of his stomach and the haze of stage fright lifted from his eyes, Ronnie implemented Draven's instructions. Collins fumbled a hand-off and lost 4 yards. Ed Pell turned the corner behind blocking from the pulling guards, Bellson and Matson, to pick up 6. On third and 8 from the 41, with the Steeler linebackers streaking in on the blitz, Ronnie sent Collins straight up the middle on the draw play. Bursting through the line, veering left in the open territory vacated by the linebackers, Collins rambled for 26 big yards before the Steelers' free safety finally tumbled him out-of-bounds on the Pittsburgh 33.

Ronnie had obviously surprised the Steelers by sticking to the running attack when the tactical situation fairly screamed for the use of the pass. Having perhaps implanted in the defense the notion that a rookie quarterback's mind was beginning to assume a similarity pattern, Ronnie reacted nicely. In the huddle he called for a play-action pass to split end Arnie Jennings, off a fullback fake into the line.

As it happened, everything worked the way it should have. The Steeler middle linebacker, whose primary responsibility in the pro 4-3 defensive set was to keep track of the enemy fullback, charged up as Ronnie faked to Collins driving through the line. Jennings slanted over the center, Ronnie hit him with a bullet, and the end was away. Tight end Frank Morris had taken the strong-side safety with him on a turn-out. The Steelers' strong-side cornerback was occupied with the flanker, George Pyle, who had gone deep on his pattern. His path thus cleared, Jennings found himself covered man-for-man by his defender and easily outraced him, following the reception, into the corner of the end zone. When Bobo Zarilla added the conversion, the Giants were back in the ball game at 31–20.

They were destined to move no closer. Both defenses tightened. The teams traded field goals in the fourth quarter, and the game ended with the New Yorkers losing their preseason opener, 34 to 23.

Ronnie Baxter felt neither discouraged nor particularly heartened by his pro debut. To him, being basically a perfectionist, it was a standoff. He had thrown a TD pass on a properly executed play. Scanning the other side of the coin, he had also been intercepted, leading to an opponent's score. At that, he did little brooding about it. Instead Ronnie put into effect the healthy attitude that had sustained him through years of junior high, high school, and college football. Good, bad, or indifferent, the Steeler game lay in the past. He could profit by his mistakes, of course, and revel in his brief moments of success. In any case, both elements formed merely a small patch on the infinitely larger fabric of the future.

At the film session three days later, Wayne Draven chewed out more than a few players for ragged performances. He was particularly distressed by the lack of continuity on offense. Ronnie was pleased when Draven threw him a crumb of praise for his play-calling and his touchdown pass to Jennings. However, Draven went on at some length and with considerable heat concerning his errant toss that the Steelers had picked off—why it had happened and how Ronnie could avoid such disaster later on.

He's tough, Ronnie thought. *Hard as a piece of sole leather, and he gets mad enough to bite roofing nails at times. But he's fair. No matter what, the coach really earns his salary. I wouldn't be in his shoes for anything.*

Ronnie sincerely meant it. For him, at the age of twenty-two, the unfolding pro football world was akin to an oyster. Time alone would disclose whether he captured the pearl or came away with only the empty shell.

4 | *A Letter Home*

ONE DAY shortly thereafter Ronnie sat down to write one of his infrequent—by necessity—letters to his folks.

"Dear Mom and Dad,

"Please forgive the week and a half between letters, but I wanted to wait until I had something concrete to tell you one way or the other. Now, at last, I have good news!

"The 'Turk' has come and gone for the last time, and he didn't get me! In other words, I've made the squad, and I'll be with the Giants to start the season when we play the Vikings in Minnesota next Sunday!

"Of course, I'm listed as number three on the depth chart at quarterback, behind Chips Farrell and Harry Flood. As I wrote earlier, Dan McComb, my first roommate, was cut. The Denver Broncos signed him, but they released him later, too. Ben Barton was put on the taxi squad and sent to play with one of our farm clubs; he'll continue to practice with us a couple of times a week.

"So, I've been pretty lucky, I guess. I'll sit and watch and learn; in addition, I'll be holding the ball for Bobo Zarilla on field goal tries and extra points. Coach Draven will have me manning the sideline phones, relaying information on our opponents' defensive tendencies from the press box spotter to the bench. At least I'll feel as though I'm doing something, even if I don't play much right now.

"As you probably know from the papers, we did pretty well in our four preseason games, if you want to call a 2–2 record that. Everyone is fairly satisfied with our showing—except for that game with Dallas. They scored twice in the last two minutes to win 24–23. That hurt! Do you know how much noise 55,000 people can make in the Cotton Bowl? As you might imagine, the film session the next week was a pretty lively affair. The coach almost had a stroke watching the movies. He was even madder than when it happened, if possible.

"We're in fairly good shape physically for the opener, considering the way these pros play for keeps.

The team has an assortment of minor injuries; nothing serious, just run-of-the-mill bumps, bruises, muscle pulls, and so on. There are a pair of major ones, too. Al McGuire, the offensive center, has two broken fingers—somebody stepped on him in the Dallas game. A shoulder separation will keep one of the defensive tackles, Jim Karnarveron, out of action for the next four or five weeks, according to Dr. Lotts.

"The New York sportswriters apparently don't think much of our chances. The Giants are a consensus pick for the middle of their Eastern Conference Division, if not worse. Wylie Jordan of the *News* even went so far as to predict that we'll only beat out the Saints and the Eagles, which would leave the team sixth in the entire Conference. Frankly, I don't agree with them. But then this is a whale of a tough league, and it isn't too easy to rebuild from a 5-8-1 record. However, if we can stay healthy, and if some of the rookies come through to help out the veterans, we should be right in there at the finish. Anyway, I hope so.

"Looking back on it, Mom and Dad, I've played some, but not nearly as much as I'd have liked. At times I want to get in there so bad I can taste it, especially when we aren't doing so well on the field. I realize that preseason games are a real headache for the coaching staff. No matter how they handle the personnel, there are going to be beefs from one quarter or another. To reduce the thing to its barest essentials, it's a time for weighing and evaluating rookies—seeing which of them will measure up to the NFL and which won't. On the other hand, the veterans—the men the coach is going up and down the line with—must be played, too. And if they don't get enough work, then they won't be ready to open the season either. It's quite a problem, and it's just one of about a thousand a pro coach has to worry about.

"I didn't sleep very well the night before the final squad cuts were made. I've really been happy here at Fairfield; I've struck up many new friendships and learned more about the inside of football than I ever dreamed existed. The possibility of having to leave the Giants depressed me no end.

"I knew my bonus and high draft status were in my favor. But people have been paid pretty well to sign before, and some of them still have wound up hearing the 'Midnight Footsteps.' I don't have to tell you I'm a perfectionist when it comes to my own performance. Wayne Draven is the same way. I can still recall how many times he told me, 'Do it again! Do it right this time!' I feel I recovered well from my shaky start in the Steeler game and did okay against the other three teams. As you'll recall from my other letters, I played anywhere from one series of downs to a full quarter and a half.

"Nevertheless, as I tossed and turned that night in camp, I could look back and see where I'd been guilty of literally dozens of mistakes: a poor play call, a mistimed hand-off that resulted in a fumble, a pass overthrown when a receiver was in the clear, a pass into a crowd to a covered man while an alternate receiver was in the clear.

"But, all that worrying is behind me now. I'm a Giant! When you catch us on TV back home, Chips Farrell will be number 17, Harry Flood 18, and I'll be 19. Look for me on the sidelines with earphones on. Ha! Ha!

"I have to run now. Viking films are on tap, plus (probably) a last tune-up quiz on our playbooks.

"Love,

"Ronnie

"P.S. Waited until I was sure I'd stick with the Giants to arrange for living quarters in New York. Right now it looks as though I'll share an apartment with Bruiser Kinarski, the boy from Cincinnati I wrote you about. As soon as we have an address, I'll send it to you.

"R."

5 | *Metropolitan Stadium*

THE PLANE ride from Kennedy airport had been fun, even though it wasn't the smoothest Ronnie could remember. The rookie quarterback enjoyed the easy companionship of his teammates, the changed attitude of the veterans toward him, and even their good-natured jokes, both verbal and practical.

There was no concealing the fact that the Giants were an edgy bunch on the eve of the season opener. Ronnie realized, as did they all, that so very much was riding on this first game. They had to prove to themselves, their fans, and the sportswriters that they could rebound from their wretched season the year before and win in a league getting tougher with each passing campaign.

Sunday dawned gray and grim, with a cool nip in

the air not at all abnormal for Minnesota, even in September. A drizzling rain commenced to fall as the squad taped. It picked up in intensity while they ate their steak, butterless baked potato, salad, and tea, and became a downpour by late morning. It slackened somewhat when the players entered the buses taking them from their motel to Metropolitan Stadium, home field of the Vikings.

Despite the weather, an overflow crowd of 50,000 fans jammed into the double-decked park. They shook the rafters with ringing roars of approval every time one of their favorites was introduced, starting with number 10, quarterback Frank Packenham, whom the local press corps had dubbed the "Scrambling Wreck from Georgia Tech." The yells redoubled in volume as the PA announcer called out the name of Herm De Hartog, the Vikings' coach, a former NFL great who had piloted his expansion team to a second-place tie in the Western Conference the previous season.

"If they go ape like this now, what'll they do when their guys score?" Ronnie wondered out loud.

"Tear the joint apart, believe you me," replied Bert Diehl, the offensive backfield coach, who happened to be standing nearby. "For my money, Ron, the three places in this league you'll hear the most noise are here, Green Bay, and Baltimore. New York used to rate right up there, too, but Yankee Stadium has been pretty quiet the last couple of years since we're losers."

With a grin, Ronnie replied, "I've got a hunch the next few months are going to change all that. There's a winning feeling in my bones, Coach."

Ronnie Baxter was no ordinary, brash, cocky, pop-off rookie. Under normal circumstances, he was a shy, awed, quiet young man who still found it almost impossible to believe he was actually standing on the sidelines of a National Football League gridiron in the uniform of the New York Giants. But he possessed a sound football instinct, and he liked what he had seen at Fairfield and in the preseason contests.

Then, as if by way of further explanation, he added, "We were twenty-six, three, and one while I was playing at Tulsa. Reckon winning became a habit with me."

Diehl nodded, his face somber. "Don't ever change, Ronnie. Power of positive thinking and all that. Your college coach, Charley Tubbs, and I have been friends for years, which is partly why you're here right now. But with all due respect to you and him, this isn't Tulsa. Well, son, time to go to work. Grab the phones. We won the toss."

From in front of the bench, Draven raised his voice. "Kick receiving unit, you're on. Offensive unit, get ready."

Hal Honegger settled under the high, end-over-ender on the goal line and brought it back out to the 27. Al McGuire, towel flapping wetly against the back of his legs as he led the troops out of the huddle, crouched over the ball at center. It took more than two broken fingers to keep him out of the lineup. Chips Farrell surveyed the defense, then shifted his eyes toward Arnie Jennings, split to the right, and across to George Pyle, flanked wide to the left.

Barking signals, Farrell took the ball on the third count, backpedaled seven steps, and set up to throw. With Don Payson and Jack Strawbridge, the two big tackles, dropping off the line on pass blocking, Farrell had time, plenty of it, to see exactly what was taking place downfield as his receivers ran their patterns. Since mud underfoot actually assists the offense and hinders the defense, mainly because potential pass catchers know exactly when they will cut while defenders don't, Farrell had hoped to connect with the bomb immediately, thus establishing a psychological edge for the Giants that could carry throughout the game.

In the pocket, the veteran quarterback sized up the developing situation in the twinkling of an eye. Collins, who had stayed back to block, now drifted out into the flat as a safety valve. The Vikings' middle linebacker hesitated between rushing the passer and covering the dangerous fullback. Tight end Frank Morris, brush-blocking at the line, went down and out, taking the strong safety with him. Arnie Jennings ran a deep pattern turn-in, well diagnosed by the weak-side cornerback. Flanker George Pyle hooked out into the short zone, only to be blanketed by George Cox, the Vikings' strong-side corner man.

With this coverage on the other receivers, running back Ed Pell, the big blue 33 showing on his uniform as he fled downfield, found himself in the position most envied by a fleet halfback—isolated one-on-one coverage by a much slower linebacker. Without so much as breaking stride, a step and a half behind his defender, he caught Farrell's pass on the 50 and set sail for the Minnesota goal.

The remaining safety, aware of what was going on too late, and mindful of his secondary responsibility to cover a halfback in the deep zone, rushed over in an attempt to head Pell off. Frank Morris, the ideal size for a tight end at six-four and 225, cut him down with a crunching block. Ed Pell waltzed into the end zone without a hand being laid on him to complete a 73-yard scoring strike on the first play from scrimmage!

Leaping wildly into the air as Pell tossed the ball toward the official's upraised arms, Ronnie Baxter ran

THROW THE LONG BOMB!

onto the field with Bobo Zarilla and the place-kicking unit. Kneeling at the 10, he handled the snap cleanly, placed it down, then both felt and heard the thud when Zarilla's sweeping toe drove through it. With only thirty-five seconds gone, the Giants were on the scoreboard at 7 to 0.

The advantage, however, was not destined to last very long. Wayne Draven stormed in vain. Ronnie passed along the suggestions of Remmie Braun and Hamlin Turner in the press box. Defensive adjustments were made. Despite all their combined efforts, the Vikings drove 80 yards in eleven plays for the equalizer. The last 15 came on a pass from Packenham to his split end, Palmer. Before it was completed, the Viking quarterback had run 30 or 40 yards back and across the field, pursued by the two Giant tackles, Paul Nestor and rookie Bill Lattington, playing due to Jim Karnarveron's injury.

The play over, Ronnie whistled in grudging admiration. "He sure *can* scramble, Coach," he said into the intercom mike to Turner. "Doesn't De Hartog believe in quarterbacks passing out of a pocket at all?"

"You kidding, Ron? Packenham's been around for five years now. Not only is he a crowd pleaser, but he gets the job done on the field, too. Don't let it bother you, though, Ron. In the long run you're better off

playing it Draven's way. Packenham has been thrown for some sizable losses, too. If Gunner Swenson hadn't slipped and fallen that time, Palmer would never have grabbed the ball. We might even have intercepted. Weather is the great leveler, so they say. It just helped them. It's our turn next."

Turner's crystal ball, like the skies lowering over Metropolitan Stadium, proved more than a bit cloudy. On the first play from scrimmage after the Minnesota kickoff, Horse Collins fumbled and Minnesota's big defensive end Dan Dowd fell on the slippery pigskin at the Giants' 29. Packenham took the Vikings down to the 8. There the attack stalled, so they were forced to settle for a fourth-down, 16-yard field goal. The first period ended with the Vikings on top, 10–7.

Midway in the second quarter Bobo Zarilla boomed a 45-yarder through the uprights to knot the count at 10–10. Subsequently, however, disaster struck the Giants from every available point of the compass, or so it seemed to Ronnie. Luck, as he well knew, was a fickle goddess; apparently there existed no rhyme or reason in the way she dispensed her favors.

Mixing his plays beautifully, Chips Farrell drove the team to a first down on the Viking 20. Calling for a quick slant-in over the middle to tight end Frank Morris, Farrell rifled the soggy ball in Morris' direction. Supposedly a quick pass thrown low and fast to lessen interception possibilities, the ball slipped off Farrell's fingertips to begin with, then was sent even farther awry as it was tipped by a charging tackle. The ball, thus up for grabs, fluttered crazily into the air, acting like a duck gunned down in flight. The Vikings' second-year linebacker, Jim Walston, leaped up, speared it on the Viking 15, and cut across the field to the far side. As the blockers formed, he ran over Chips Farrell, the last man to have a shot at him, and completed an 85-yard scoring play.

A tremendous roar of joyous approval welled from the packed stands, being repeated when the gun sounded ending the first half. The Vikings still led, 17–10.

If the initial thirty minutes had been painful, the second half was positively excruciating for Draven and the Giants. They were buried. Everything that could have gone wrong did. It was the Steeler preseason game all over again. Pass blocking broke down, although Draven substituted at tackle and fullback in an effort to repel the boarders who kept swarming onto the backfield decks. Mechanical errors cropped up, then fumbles and mix-ups in assignments. Farrell's necessarily hurried passes were off target. Flood, in a brief stint, did no better. Receivers zigged when they should have zagged. On other occasions they simply dropped the ball.

Interminably the long, wet, dreary afternoon wore along. At last the referee walked toward the Giant bench, holding up two fingers to indicate that much time remained in the game. Glancing at the scoreboard, which read Vikings 45, Giants 13, Ronnie Baxter thought wryly to himself that the official's two-minute warning signal was the best news the team had received since Farrell's opening touchdown bomb.

Wayne Draven, face bleak and angry, approached. "All right, Ron," he snapped. "Get in there. Let's see how you operate under actual game conditions. You call the plays. You're on your own. Do the best you can. I don't expect any miracles."

Adjusting the chin strap on his helmet, Ron raced onto the field, his mind awhirl. A muddy Chips Farrell passed him on the way to the bench.

"Good luck, kid," Farrell called. "I hope yours'll be better than mine. They're tough. I haven't been on my back so much since I broke a leg in high school."

The ball rested on the Giants' 38. Viewing the situation objectively, Ronnie acknowledged there was little hope except to put the ball in the air and try to connect for a TD that would serve to make the final score look a little more respectable.

The Viking defenders, of course, had the same idea. They blitzed ferociously, extending to Ronnie the customary welcome an untried young signal caller could expect in the NFL. Even the safety man rushed in. Dropping back the normal seven paces, Ronnie winced under the weight of the assault. Pursued, harassed, menaced, he desperately tried to spot an uncovered receiver downfield. He ran to his right, reversed his field, found the left no better. More than a quarter-ton of Vikings toppled him back on the 28 for a 10-yard loss.

Returning to the huddle, Ronnie had gained a valuable insight into one facet of the incredibly complicated pro quarterback's job. To wit: A pass pocket remained one only as long as the protection kept it so. After that, Draven's philosophy about scrambling quarterbacks or no, you had to flee for your life and pray that you fell gently when hit and didn't break anything.

Having survived his first determined pro blitz in a game that counted, at the cost of a long loss, Ronnie took stock. Despite the lopsided score, Ronnie decided the time had arrived for him to match wits with the defenders. In other, more favorable situations, he would be called upon to outfox people bent on separating his head from his shoulders. Since Wayne

Draven had indicated to him that he was on his own, Ronnie drew a deep breath and culled one small nugget from the mountain of informational ore that had been fed, computer-like, into his brain.

If the truth be known, Ronnie Baxter was somewhat thankful for the blitz that had ground him into the mire, because it brought him quickly to the basic realities of the National Football League. Second and 20 from the 28. Undoubtedly the red dog would be on again. How best to combat it, considering the ragged performance of his weary pass blockers?

Without hesitation, he called the play in the huddle, rapping the words out with a ring of authority. "Blue right. X fly, Y deep, Z short sideline turn-out. Forty-nine slip screen to Collins. On one. Ready, break."

At the first "Hut!" Ronnie grasped the exchange, dropped straight back, noted his pass protection was halfway improved, pump-faked once deep, and coolly allowed the onrushing defenders to almost reach him. Then Ronnie flipped the leather into the left flat to Collins, who had made brief contact with a dark-jerseyed Viking, after which he had drifted a few steps to the outside. A wall of Giants escorted Collins down the sideline, and they did their jobs well. They erased all but the safety, Don Andrews. The latter managed to slip a block thrown at him by Don Payson and wrestle the ball carrier to earth on the Viking 11. Over-all, the play had gained a total of 61 yards.

With fifty-eight seconds left, the Giants scored their consolation TD. Ronnie handed off to Ed Pell on a slant over the left side from three yards out. Moments later time ran out. The Giants had undergone a dismal season opener in losing to the Minnesota Vikings, 45–20.

In marked contrast to the optimistic gaiety that had prevailed on the plane leaving New York, a spirit of unrelieved gloom hung over the Giants during the return trip. They had not only been beaten, but beaten badly. Their minds were heavy with the knowledge they had done little to help their own cause. Of the 45 Viking points, 28 had been directly due to offensive lapses and fumbles. In addition the one-sided game had extracted a heavy physical toll. There was, of course, the normal collection of bruises, sprains, scrapes, and bumps. Worse, Jack Strawbridge, an offensive tackle, and Al Waskoff, the 275-pound de-fensive end, had been left behind in a Minneapolis hospital for precautionary X rays. Both had taken shots to the head and had apparently been the victims of concussions.

Although down in the dumps over the loss, Ronnie

71

had no cause to feel disconsolate about his individual effort. He had lived through his first red dog, called a play that foiled the second, reorganized a badly battered and shaken team, and led it on a last-minute touchdown sortie. In two short minutes, Ronnie thought to himself as the plane hovered over the Kennedy complex preparatory to landing, he had gained more confidence in his ability to compete than he had at Fairfield or during the preseason tilts. He realized that it required three years, possibly four, for the development of a competent pro quarterback. Even granting that, he felt he was on his way, and he glowed a little inside.

As the team gathered at the terminal to reclaim their baggage, Wayne Draven's parting shot to them snatched Ronnie abruptly out of his cozy cocoon of self-satisfaction.

"Enjoy your day off tomorrow, boys," the coach said dourly. "We've got the Cardinals coming up in St. Louis next Sunday. With them, blitzing is a way of life. They and the Cowboys have been picked to win the Eastern Conference. Need I say more? Your tongues will be hanging out by Friday, that I promise you. Be prepared." With that, he turned on his heel and strode out.

Between game films illuminating all the mistakes

at Metropolitan Stadium and others involving the resurgent Cardinals, plus practice on the field itself,
Ronnie Baxter looked forward to a very tough week
indeed.

6 | The Giants Regroup

WAYNE DRAVEN kept his word.

Tuesday, Wednesday, and Thursday were pure, un-adulterated murder. To compound the discomfort, the weather decided not to cooperate. More than a week after Labor Day, with fall theoretically approaching, summer returned with a vengeance for a last-ditch stand. Temperatures soared into the mid-nineties. Well-conditioned though they were, Draven's athletes drooped and wilted on the practice turf, sweated pro-fusely, and rinsed their mouths with gallons of Yogi Di Orio's sickly green citrus concoction they had de-risively dubbed "Battery Acid." They sucked ice cubes, draped towels soaked in ice water around their necks, rushed the sideline oxygen canisters, and cursed a schedule that compelled them to play football in the middle of a tropical heat wave.

On the gridiron, Draven alternately blew his whistle, groaned, rolled his eyes heavenward, and shouted, "Again! Do it again! Let's get it right this time!" The Giants, although they might have run the same play in what they considered perfect fashion on five consecutive occasions, would line up and go through it a sixth, or a seventh, or an eighth time.

Taking his turn at leading the offense in dummy scrimmage, Ronnie Baxter shook his head to clear away some of the perspiration dripping into his eyes. In the huddle, he took a few seconds' breather, turning to Ed Pell.

"Whew! I'm bushed! How about you?"

Pell was forthright in his reply. "You serious? If they did this to horses, the Society for the Prevention of Cruelty to Animals would be after 'em. But then we're not animals. We're only football players."

"I thought pro teams took it easy on all this stuff once the season started," said Ronnie.

"Draven's teams don't," Pell said with a wry grin. "Especially not after the way we were driven out of the state of Minnesota last Sunday. You'd better call a play, Ronnie, or he'll have us taking five laps."

If the physical activities on the field were taxing, the mental anguish at the film sessions topped them a hundredfold. At least in an area of 7,200 square yards there was a small possibility, Ronnie reflected, of hiding oneself temporarily—of blending chameleon-like into the surrounding background and perhaps escaping some of the sting of Wayne Draven's hyperactive tongue. In the filmroom, however, no such opportunity existed. Every man was under the coach's eye constantly, writhing and squirming as the concrete evidence of that horrible afternoon at Metropolitan Stadium unfolded; it was a truly captive audience wincing under Draven's caustic and often sarcastic comments. No one was spared, Ronnie included.

The offensive line seemed to be a particular target. Like many teams in the league, the Giants' coaches graded each player on his performance in each game. Assistant coach Al Bradshaw, in whose charge the members of the offensive line had been placed, read off the grade figures for the Viking game.

"Don Payson, forty-six percent. Booker T. Bellson, forty-eight percent. Al McGuire was the real star; he scored a sparkling fifty-five percent. Bill Matson, fifty-two percent. Jack Strawbridge, thirty-nine percent. Gentlemen, let's not mince words. Last Sunday you couldn't have beaten a girls' touch-football team. You were unbelievably bad. And you all know why and how. Pass blocking was almost nonexistent. Nobody, but nobody, was picking up the blitzers. On running plays I've seen better holes opened by my ten-year-old son. We were particularly weak on the power-lead sweeps and pitchouts. Coach?"

Wayne Draven rose, letting his eyes sweep quickly around the room before he began.

"Okay, Al. Thanks. Well, you offensive linemen, there you have it. Not very much to be proud of, huh? The best did his job a little over half the time. The worst, only a third. You're not going to win in this league with that kind of sloppy performance. But I don't see any sense wasting time crying over spilled milk. My job is to make sure last Sunday's fiasco isn't repeated. Mike, if you'll get the lights we'll run over these game films again."

Painstakingly, in detail, drawing on the sum total of thirty-odd years' experience in the professional game, Draven reran the movies; he stopped the action as many as a dozen times, sometimes reversing the film, until a mistake was pointed out and its remedy deeply implanted in its perpetrator's mind.

With the individual performances evaluated, the decks were thus cleared by Thursday. Then the game plan evolved. Prior Cardinal films were shown. Draven and the staff pinpointed two potential weaknesses in the St. Louis defense: a rookie cornerback playing in place of an injured veteran, and the team's go-for-broke blitzing tendencies. The Cardinals' veteran free safety, Len Weston, who had led the league in pass interceptions the year before and had accounted for two thefts in the opening game, was spotlighted. His deft, daring moves, quick reflexes, and gambling techniques all showed up when Draven explained them.

By Friday afternoon the Giants, determined to redeem themselves, were just about ready to tear apart any enemy football player foolish enough to get in their way. After the tapering-off practice of wind sprints and padless signal drills, Wayne Draven drove the final psychological nail into the structure of a grueling week's work.

Into the clubhouse, which smelled of liniment, chlorine, sweat, wet towels, and cigar smoke, he strode, bearing a folded newspaper clipping in his hand. The easy conversation died away. Draven's gaze first swept into the crowded training room, Yogi Di Orio's domain, and noted Jim Karnarveron, his arm still in a black sling, leaning against the farther wall tilting a Coke to his mouth. A naked Don Payson was stretched out on the rubbing table, his back muscles being kneaded by an assistant trainer. Arnie Jennings lounged in the whirlpool bath, on whose gleaming side some wag

had printed in red marking pencil, ROOKIES ARE FOR-
BIDDEN TO MAKE COFFEE IN THIS RECEPTICAL. Directly
beneath, a second unknown author had added, SWEN-
SON MUST HAVE WRITTEN THIS. NOBODY ELSE ON THE
CLUB SPELLS THAT BADLY.

Draven held up his hand for attention. "You all
know the flight time tomorrow. Be there thirty minutes
early. By the way, here's a little item from the *Post-
Dispatch* I thought you might be interested in." He
thumbtacked it to the cork bulletin board, then ambled
out.

The Giants, curious, crowded around. Nobody said
anything, nor were words needed. The clipping from
the St. Louis newspaper was self-explanatory.

In bold, black letters, the headline read: "CARDI-
NALS FAVORED BY 13 OVER NEW YORK IN
STADIUM TILT."

Suddenly Lou Slabodnick, the chunky left linebacker, yelled, "This is one set of books that's going to
take a beating, eh, fellows?" His teammates gave forth
a thunderous whoop of approval in which Ronnie
Baxter heartily joined.

Like the coach or not, Ronnie admitted with a
twinge of admiration, Wayne Draven must be rated
a master strategist. Here were a bunch of pros shouting like college kids, anxious to erase the bitter memory

of their failure against the Vikings and eager to confound the experts who had established the Cardinals as heavy favorites. For the past three days Draven had driven, cajoled, tongue-lashed—done everything in his power to get them mentally "up" for the forthcoming game.

Yet, now, in a single, simple stroke, he had seemingly done more to prepare the Giants than the sum total of his previous efforts.

Ronnie grinned on his way to the shower. It was great to be a pro football player. Above all, it was great to be a New York Giant. And thirteen more Sundays lay ahead in which to prove that he belonged.

7 | *Draven Speaks His Mind*

WHATEVER THE ingredients of Wayne Draven's particular brand of psychological medicine, they proved effective.

As underdogs often will in the topsy-turvy National Football League, the Giants dismembered the Cardinals with clean, surgical precision. Before a standing-room-only crowd at the new Busch Memorial Stadium, they stormed to a first-quarter TD and field goal, added another 6-pointer before the half on a Farrell to Morris bomb good for 66 yards, and led 17–3 at intermission.

With the Cardinals forced to play catch-up football via a constant aerial attack, the Giants forged ahead 24–3 midway in the third period. Lyndon Bentley, New York's strong safety, snatched an errant Earl Lat-

timer toss and ran it back 45 yards to the Cardinals'
10. Horse Collins slashed over from the 2. Bobo Zarilla
kicked another field goal of 31 yards, and the Cardinals eked out a "so what?" touchdown with but twelve
seconds left. The final score, in an upset, was Giants
27, Cardinals 10.

The offensive line did yeoman work all afternoon,
keeping Cardinal red-doggers away from Chips Farrell, allowing the veteran quarterback to "throw out
of the rocking chair." The defensive unit was nothing
short of magnificent. St. Louis gained a mere 176 yards
overall, of which only 35 came via rushing.

The following Sunday, September twenty-fourth,
the Giants embarked on their third consecutive road
game of the young season. Their landlords, the baseball Yankees, wound up the American League campaign on the road. Hence, the Stadium would become
available for football when the Philadelphia Eagles
furnished the opposition for the home opener October
first. The Giants marked time by crushing the New
Orleans Saints, 33 to 7.

The Giants very nearly blew the Eagle contest,
frittering away 14–0 and 21–10 leads. A safety blitz,
the Eagles' favorite defensive maneuver, bothered the
New Yorkers considerably in the late periods, forcing
two fumbles that cost 10 points. Deep in the final

quarter, the ball belonged to Philadelphia on their 28. Time was running out. The Giants led, 21 to 20. Quarterback Herb Hassler started picking up yardage overhead in short chunks.

With 64,000 Giant fans dying a little on each play, the Eagles moved downfield, battling both the clock and the New York defense. The latter, in a "prevent" setup, grudgingly yielded the short, inside, sideline stuff to negate the possibility of the big gainer. The clock showed thirty-three seconds left to play. Hassler was faced with a fourth-and-7 situation from the Giant 43. Another completion would accomplish two important objectives: assure the Eagles of retaining possession, and move them into at least extreme field goal range.

Hassler threw to his flanker on a quick down-and-out designed to pick up the needed yardage and carry the receiver out-of-bounds, thus stopping the clock. "Bull" Durham, the Giants' strong-side linebacker, guessing right, thought he saw an opportunity to make a gambling interception, stalling the Eagles' chances for good. He drove forward, trying to time his move perfectly, and jumped in front of the flanker. Both men went up together; both pairs of hands clawed for the ball. Durham missed getting a hand on it, but he threw the flanker's timing off and the ball fell harmlessly to the ground. However, in so doing, Durham accidentally hooked the would-be receiver's arm. An official was on top of the play, as he should have been. The latter threw his yellow penalty flag, making the pushing motion with his arms, palms front, that signaled pass interference.

A huge groan went up from the spectators, for the defensive foul carried with it an automatic first down at the spot of the infraction, which was the New York 35. Twenty-eight seconds remained on the clock— plenty of time for Hassler to call three pass plays and perhaps move the ball still closer to the goal. If he could, Norm Kramer, the Eagles' kicking specialist, would have a virtual chip shot at the game-winning three-pointer.

On first down Hassler was chased relentlessly by Paul Nestor, the right tackle, and had to toss the ball out-of-bounds, in the general direction of his safety-valve man, to keep from being buried for a long loss. A second passing attempt gained 7. A third failed, and nine seconds were left. The Philadelphia field goal unit came on. Hassler knelt on the Giant 35, halfway between the hash mark and dead center. Arms hanging loosely, head down, Kramer waited for the snap from center.

As Hassler touched the ball down and Kramer swung

THROW THE LONG BOMB!

his foot into its upward arc, with 64,000 throats suddenly stilled by the late-game drama unfolding, a blue jersey erupted high in the path of the rocketing football. Hands upstretched, fingers curved like the talons of a predatory bird seeking its prey, rookie Bill Lattington, still playing in place of the injured Jim Karnarveron, met the ball with his chest. Thus blocked, it caromed away, squirting over the near sideline!

The resultant volume of noise from the Bronx must surely have shattered windows as far south as Battery Park. Wave on wave of sound engulfed the Stadium, nor did it truly ebb even when the Giants ran one play into the line, a sneak by Harry Flood. The Giants had tripped the Eagles, 21 to 20, for their third straight win!

Later, in the steaming, happy jungle that was the New York locker room, Ronnie Baxter peeled off his clean, sweatless uniform and pondered the strange bounces a football sometimes takes. Out of the corner of his eye, he saw a knot of newsmen and radio announcers gathered around Bill Lattington's dressing cubicle, firing questions at the apple-cheeked, 280-pound youngster from Notre Dame. For just a fleeting instant a thrill of envy coursed through Ronnie's whole being as he watched his teammate relive his moment of triumph. Why, he wondered, had Fate singled Lattington out to make a contribution to victory so much greater than his own?

Then Ronnie's normally even temperament reasserted itself. He dismissed the thought as unworthy, meaningless. What was it Wayne Draven had said, opening the orientation lecture at Fairfield a couple of months ago? "Plenty of you have been stars in college, and you have the press clippings to prove it. My advice is—forget about them, quick. You can't eat press clippings, and you sure don't win games in the National Football League with them." Ronnie shrugged. There were many objects that needed years to mature and become useful. Along with good cheese and rare wine, a pro quarterback could be included in the list. His turn, he told himself, would come.

Ronnie dressed slowly, savoring the tangible aura of accomplishment, of well-being, that blankets a clubhouse following a hard-fought win. He shaved as soon as he stepped out of the shower. Bruiser Kinarski had arranged a double date with two young ladies he knew.

Ronnie worked the razor carefully around his chin. Despite the fact his mental processes were back on an even keel, there was no denying, Ronnie conceded, that *his* participation in their third straight victory had been virtually nil. He had manned the phones. He had held the ball when Bobo Zarilla kicked. That was all.

"Not that I'm complaining," he muttered to his lathered image in the mirror as he surveyed his upper lip. "It's just that I'm not used to sitting around. Of course I'm learning by observing Chips Farrell. But he'll be the Giants' quarterback for the next ten years. Where the heck do I fit into the scheme of things?"

"Got a minute before you leave, Ronnie?"

The rookie quarterback whirled at the sound of the voice and stared into Wayne Draven's relaxed face.

"Sure, Coach. Soon as I finish dressing." Ronnie wondered why Draven had sought him out.

"Good. I'll be in my office."

Ten minutes later Ronnie knocked on the door. "Come in. It's open," Draven called.

The Giants' mentor sprawled back in a padded swivel chair, legs crossed comfortably atop the littered desk. Draven waved a cigar expansively, indicating that Ronnie might sit if he chose.

"I never thought I'd live through that one," said Draven. "Too close for comfort. If Lattington hadn't seen a little daylight and broken through, we were almost certain losers. I was proud of everybody out there today."

Ronnie smiled. "I don't think I could stand being a coach. It's tough enough being a player and standing on the sidelines. But it was a tremendous win."

"Uh-huh. My sentiments exactly. I guess you're asking yourself why I called you in here, aren't you, Ronnie?"

The blond, brush-cut head nodded in agreement.

"Well, I'll tell you. I haven't been around football for thirty years or more without noticing a few things, especially concerning rookies who've made it big in college and who have to be messenger boys in pro ball until they get hep to what it's all about. It does something to them, I know. You're no exception. I can read it from your look. You may think, Ron, that with forty players to keep track of, plus preparing for a game each week and all the rest of it, I've been giving you the fast shuffle. Am I right so far?"

"Yes and no, Coach," Ronnie hedged. "There are times I feel I'm the forgotten man. Other times I want to run out on the field and play so bad it shrivels me. It's just—impatience, I suppose. I know Rome wasn't built in a day, but I can't help wishing it had been. I realize I'm soaking up know-how by watching and listening and handling the phones, and that is the way it has to be. Want me to level with you, Coach?"

"Please do," Draven said.

"My biggest worry isn't any of those. It's that I may get rusty sitting around."

Draven regarded the glowing end of his cigar. He had suspected as much. They, the kids, all wound up with it sooner or later, he thought. The yen to play. The desire to speed the processes of time, to compress months and years into minutes and hours. The senseless fear of losing skills they were just beginning to develop. It was only part of the usual pattern and had to be handled accordingly.

"Ronnie, I suspect more than once since Fairfield you could have cheerfully shot me. Let me hasten to assure you, you aren't a minority of one. But I've a job to do, and I do it my way, the way I think is best. Some players you drive. A few you appeal to. Still others you sit down and have a private talk with. You're in that last category."

Baxter felt abashed. There was more than a kernel of truth in Draven's conversation. He was considerably impressed by his coach and gratified that he would take the time to thus converse with him on such frank, openly friendly terms.

"Sir, I appreciate what you're doing," Ronnie said. "You have no idea how much. You're right. A few doubts have crept in now and then. Not of you, but myself. Maybe I was an All-American at Tulsa. Yet, deep down, I'm just a boy from a small town in Oklahoma who still can't find his way around New York and keeps staring up at the buildings. At times I get lonely. Every so often I'm scared none of this will last, that I'll wake up some morning and find these past few months were all a beautiful dream and nothing else."

"I can guess how you feel," replied Draven sympathetically. "I went through it all, my rookie season. So did Bert Diehl, Hamlin Turner, all the people on my staff. The NFL was a lot younger in those days, and in many ways a lot tougher, particularly on first-year men. You pretty much sank or swam on your own.

"What I'm trying to say is this. Don't ever question that I know you're around. The owners of this club drafted you ahead of a lot of good talent, paid you a pretty good sum for signing a contract, and gave you a fair salary to boot. You have a tremendous amount of potential, Ron. We're aware of it, or we wouldn't have gone to all that trouble.

"Nevertheless, you've got to concede there are problems. In the first place, the team is going surprisingly well. I'm not especially astonished, mind you, because I felt from the start this could be our year if certain elements fell into place. Up to now, they have. No, I'm referring to the learned writers and football experts who picked us to finish close to the bottom. We're a game out of the Division leadership. I won't rest until we're looking back at the other three teams, daring them to catch up.

"Secondly, while a game's in progress I'm juggling a million and one things around in my head. Offense. Defense. Adjustments. My assistants upstairs. The info you relay. Injuries. Substitutions. The clock. I could continue for an hour. So if it sometimes seems to you that I'm looking right through you, like you weren't even there, you'll understand why. Was Charley Tubbs any different?"

Ronnie conjured up a vision of his old college coach on the bench, then shook his head. "No, sir. He had the same pressures from the same sources. There was only one major difference. I had no leisure to think about it. I was busy on the field whenever we had the ball."

"Agreed," said Draven. "And up here you're not. Granted, it seems tough, but those are the facts of pro football life. Nothing personal, Ronnie, of course. Someday you'll be a great quarterback. When you are, another green kid'll be pacing the sidelines, thinking similar thoughts. Just take my advice. Don't try to hasten that day. Leave it to my judgment. That's what

I draw checks for on the first and fifteenth of every month. Making decisions."

Draven rose and held out his hand. Ronnie grabbed it, feeling immeasurably better than he had in a long time.

"Thanks, Coach," he said, with heartfelt, genuine gratitude. "See you Tuesday."

"You'd better. I've cooked up a couple of new plays to use against the Redskins in Washington. I figure maybe you'd do well to know about them, along with my other quarterbacks."

The two men, middle-aged and young, laughed together. Ronnie was amazed at the rapport that suddenly seemed to have sprung up between him and his coach. It had stemmed from their mutual unburdening, the recently concluded thrashing out of problems real and fancied. Ronnie felt almost close to Draven for the first time.

Furthermore, he marveled at the insight Draven had shown. The coach had delved deeply into his innermost thoughts, cleaving directly to the core of his anxiety, removing and destroying it. To the titles of teacher, leader, worrier supreme, and master architect in the rebuilding of the Giant team, Ronnie now knew he could hang one more label on Wayne Draven.

Mind reader.

Ronnie eagerly devoured the Monday morning New York dailies. Both *Times* and *News* told their by-lined stories. The Eastern Conference standings spoke for themselves. Even at this early date, Dallas seemed to have the Capitol Division title wrapped up, although Washington was reported as having "dark horse" possibilities. However, in the Century Division a tight three-team dogfight was developing. Cleveland led the pack with a 4-0 record, while New York and St. Louis followed close behind, tied at 3-1.

On October eighth, the Giants pulverized the Redskins, 34 to 14, in D.C. Stadium. The Browns kept ahead by shading the Eagles, 28–24. With New York 4-1, and Cleveland sporting a perfect 5-0 record, Sunday's forthcoming slate of games could produce interesting results in terms of Division leadership. St. Louis entertained Cleveland, and New York was being visited by the charging Dallas Cowboys.

Every NFL date had to be considered crucial. For New York, that October fifteenth shaped up as uncommonly so.

8 | *A Fearful Price to Pay*

A BRILLIANT sun, beaming down on the hordes pouring into Yankee Stadium, took most of the bite from the chill of an early autumn day. Latecomers hurried toward seats, clutching transistor radios, listening avidly to the WNEW broadcast. Hawkers of hot dogs, peanuts, and programs rent the crisp air with their strident cries. Old friends in adjacent season-ticket locations greeted each other. Breathless anticipation reigned; the tense, pre-kickoff moment was at hand. The scene was part and parcel of America's greatest spectator sport, professional football. The Giants and the Cowboys were meeting in New York with a share of the Century Division leadership at stake for the Giants, and all was right with the world!

The Cowboys won the toss and elected to receive.

Zarilla booted the ball high to the left side. Hank Wallace, of the Giants' suicide squad, brought the deep man, Rick Cable, down on the Dallas 16.

In the I formation, one of their eight or ten offensive sets, Cowboy quarterback Dave Monroe had fullback Paul Parsons as middleman. Max Waters at running back was immediately behind Parsons. The split end, Bill Barton, a 9.1 hundred-yard sprinter and Olympic gold medal winner, came wide left. Both tight end and flanker were in relatively close.

"They'll probably start with that fullback dive series right off the bat," Remmie Braun said over the telephone to Ronnie. "I can smell it. Hope Lewis and Slabodnick remember what they're supposed to do on this play. If they take the fake they're in big trouble."

"Don't sweat it, Coach," Ronnie answered. "We looked at Dallas game films this past week until our eyeballs just about fell out. They'll handle it okay."

Both Remmie Braun and Ron Baxter had hit the nail on the head. As Monroe, with the ball, spun around, the Cowboys' left guard, along with Max Waters, the deep back, moved to the left in an effort to influence the defense. Parsons took the hand-off, driving up the gut behind the blocking of the offensive center on Ron Lewis, the Giants' middle linebacker. Lewis battled him, threw him aside, careened past, and nailed Parsons before the latter was more than a yard beyond the line of scrimmage. The crowd voiced its approval. Ronnie felt the team had gained a valuable psychological lift in stopping the enemy's bread-and-butter running play immediately.

"Beautiful!" Remmie Braun yelled. "Just beautiful. Now if Turner's gang can keep double coverage on Barton without letting any other receivers get gay, we're in clover."

Overeager, the Giant defense leaped off side on the next play, leaving a second down with but four to go. They atoned by corralling Waters on a deep pitch for a three-yard loss. Faced with a third-and-long situation, Monroe tried to hit Bill Barton on a fly pattern. Gunner Swenson and Lyndon Bentley blanketed him, batting the ball away.

Dallas kicking specialist Darrell Forrester hoisted a big, high, spiraling boomer that drove the Giant safeties, George Pyle and Bill Johnson, inside their own 15. Making an over-the-shoulder catch, Pyle swung and started back upfield from the 13. Interference converged in front of him. He set sail down the middle, running well. Encountering heavy traffic at about the 35, the fleet Pyle swivel-hipped by one would-be tackler and veered sharply to the near side-line seeking some maneuvering room. Nearly pinched in, Pyle broke a second tackle, then performed an elegant cutback at the 50.

In Dallas territory at last, Pyle had only the kicker, Darrell Forrester, to beat. Under a full head of steam, with the promised land in sight and everybody in the Stadium going absolutely berserk, Pyle faked left, then reversed right, leaving Forrester stretched on the ground futilely grasping empty air. Nothing was left now except yard markers, and Pyle fled across them to the goal line. It had been an 87-yard TD jaunt with a punt return! Bobo Zarilla split the uprights, and the Giants had drawn first blood, 7 to 0.

Monroe brought his team driving right back. He passed for two first downs, using Barton as a decoy and throwing instead to his tight end and fullback. He sent Paul Parsons through a gaping hole in the middle on a draw that gained 12 and another first down. With the ball on the Giant 33, Monroe, rushed, threw incomplete, intended for Barton.

On second and 10, sensing a blitz brewing among the linebackers, Monroe called an audible at the line, designed to send Max Waters, the halfback, into the short hook zone which a full-scale red dog might leave relatively vacant. The play call was perfect, except for one small detail that Monroe could not have foreseen. Backpedaling furiously, he slipped and partially lost his balance, plus valuable time. When he recovered, both Ron Lewis and Bull Durham, the Giants' middle and right linebackers, had wrapped him up.

In his anxiety to make the kill, however, Durham had grabbed Monroe by the face mask. The resultant penalty moved the Cowboys all the way to the New York 18 with a first down. There the defense stiffened. Andy Robertson, the left end, broke through to dump Monroe for an 11-yard loss. A running play gained 5 back. Barton dropped a Monroe pass on the 10. So, with fourth and 16 from the 24, Darrell Forrester rammed home a 31-yard field goal which closed the gap to 7—3. The score stood that way as the first quarter drew to a close.

Midway in the second stanza Forrester connected again, this time from 46 yards out, making it Giants 7, Cowboys 6, in a tough defensive battle.

Late in the period the Giants' offense began to pick up in tempo. Following a short punt off the side of Forrester's foot, the New Yorkers found themselves in excellent field position on their own 37.

Chips Farrell wasted not a second taking to the air lanes. Back in the pocket, benefiting from hard-nosed pass protection, he threw to Ed Pell, who had gone deep on a simple fly pattern and outrun his defender near the far sideline. The Dallas free safety finally got over and knocked Pell out-of-bounds, but the overall gain was 31 yards, all the way down to the Cowboys' 32.

On first down Farrell missed George Pyle, the flanker, slanting quickly over the middle. Horse Collins picked up four on a power sweep left.

Impatiently bouncing up and down on the sidelines near the Giant bench, Ronnie Baxter viewed the action with mixed emotions. He hoped, naturally, that the team would take the ball in. On the other hand, should a field goal become the strategy, he'd be in the thick of things, if only for a brief instant, handling his ball-holding assignment.

With third and 6, Farrell tried to outguess the defense by calling for a draw to Collins in an obvious passing situation. Dallas was waiting, however, and stopped the fullback for no gain.

With fourth down at hand, Ronnie, Bobo Zarilla, and the rest of the kicking unit trotted into the game. Kneeling on the 35-yard line, Ronnie stared in stern concentration, hands outstretched, at the ball through the legs of center Al McGuire.

McGuire chose that particular juncture to uncork his only really poor snap in two seasons. Taking off erratically, the ball spiraled high above Ronnie's fingers and slightly to the left.

Ronnie strained upward to grab it. In his haste to find the handle, he juggled it momentarily. With no possible chance now to get the ball down on the turf for Zarilla to kick it, Ronnie tucked it under his arm and started drifting to the right, seeking some kind of opening.

Frank Morris, the Giants' tight end, had blocked his man at the line. Then, sparing a fleeting glance at the tangled backfield situation, figuring Ronnie needed help, Morris angled down and out, only to find himself alone near the sideline. The Dallas secondary had held fast for an instant. Then they had instinctively closed to defend against Ronnie's seemingly hopeless spur-of-the-moment attempt to gain the yardage necessary for a first down.

About to be obliterated by two burly linemen, the rookie quarterback spotted Morris' blue jersey and white number 87 in the narrowing gap between his pursuers. Desperately, without being able to gauge the distance accurately, Ronnie heaved the ball in Morris' direction as he was falling to the ground. Although lying under Cowboy beef, he knew from the great clamor that arose that something good must have happened.

When he was finally able to regain his feet, Ronnie saw Frank Morris rolling in the end zone with the ball

clutched to his chest and an official's upraised arms signaling a touchdown!

Of all the delicious things, Ronnie thought with a bursting sense of happy pride, *a 6-pointer on a busted field goal try!*

When Zarilla booted the conversion that brought the count to 14–6 in favor of the Giants, Ronnie loped off the field. Wayne Draven stood at the sideline, waiting.

His face savage, Draven snarled, "As if a coach doesn't have enough trouble winning in this league, he's forced to stand by and watch fouled-up center snaps and butterfingered ball holders on a field goal attempt."

Ronnie froze, jaw hanging open, unable to believe his ears for a second or two. By then Draven had tired of playing his little joke and relented. Grinning broadly, he added, "Fortunately, my holder is also a kid with something besides cotton batting stuffed inside his skull. That was quick thinking, Ronnie. One of the marks of a real pro is the ability to improvise, to turn impending disaster into seven on the scoreboard. You just did it. Nice going."

Ronnie gulped, nodded, and sat down on the bench. Would he ever get accustomed to Draven's mercurial mood changes, his bizarre sense of humor? Although

Ronnie assured himself he had reacted well in an emergency, he was smart enough to evaluate the impromptu touchdown pass to Morris as the rankest sort of luck, a million-to-one shot that might not recur in a dozen years.

The Giants took their 14–6 lead into the locker room with them at half time. The final thirty minutes produced no touchdowns for either team, a field goal apiece, and a season's high for clean, purposeful head-knocking. The mayhem grew apace as the game wore on; the roster of walking and limping wounded on both sides increased alarmingly. For the Giants, Arnie Jennings was helped off with a badly sprained ankle. Bill Matson suffered a broken hand. Andy Robertson took the full brunt of a devastating blind-side block. He fell heavily, knocked senseless. Examined by Dr. Lotts, the team physician, he was sent to the hospital for X rays.

Thus the Giants beat the Cowboys, 17 to 9, but paid a fearful price in the process. Doctor, trainer, and assistants all worked overtime that evening, patching up various minor hurts. Some players would return, although at a reduced level of efficiency, against the Steelers a week hence. Others would not, and Wayne Draven was faced with the vexing problem of shifting personnel to fill the gaps in the Giant ranks.

On the bright side, the Giants now owned a neat five-game winning streak. With a 5-1 record, they reigned atop the Century Division standings, thanks to some outside help. Cleveland had fallen before a fired-up St. Louis team, and now the Division was dead-locked in a fierce three-way tie for first place.

Ben Teague, in his Monday morning *Times* column, wrote: "Ronnie Baxter, the rookie quarter-back from Tulsa the Giants are bringing along slowly, displayed a rare and cool presence of mind in the midst of the botched FG try. The youngster, whom Wayne Draven and the New York brass insist will one day fill the king-size shoes left vacant a few years ago by the 'Bald Eagle' and 'Chuckin' Chester,' turned a chaotic broken play into a near-miracle TD. There's no getting around the truism that 7 points are infinitely better than 3. Come to think of it, Wayne Draven ought to incorporate the zany goings-on into the Giants' playbook. It might come in handy in the future when things are rough and the Giants need a lift."

Ronnie carefully cut out the article and pasted it into the scrapbook he had started back at Fairfield. It didn't contain much yet, but Ronnie realized it was simply because he hadn't done very much yet. The weeks and months to come could well change all that, he thought. He hoped so. A serious, levelheaded boy, Ronnie Baxter had listened diligently to the advice of his father and his high school and college coaches. As a result he let none of Teague's laudatory prose either becloud his judgment or impair his determination. He had, he knew, traveled a significant distance since the July morning of his arrival at training camp. A long, hard road still remained, though; heartache, frustration, and a longer period of apprenticeship would undoubtedly be his lot before he ever started a game at quarterback for the New York Giants.

Sobered by the thought, Ronnie was nevertheless pleased on two counts as he softly closed the scrapbook cover in order not to awaken his still-snoring roommate, Bruiser Kinarski.

He and Wayne Draven had reached a more complete understanding with each other. In addition Ronnie had learned that luck, if only one were prepared to wait a sufficient length of time, had a way of evening matters up eventually.

Whistling tunelessly, Ronnie padded on slippered feet into the apartment's tiny kitchen to make the morning coffee.

9 | *Troubles Come Not Singly*

WE WON THE battle," said Wayne Draven ominously to the Giant writers assembled at the weekly Quarterback Club luncheon on the Monday after the Dallas donnybrook, "but a few more victories like that and we'll wind up losing the war. Yogi Di Orio and Dr. Lotts combined can hardly cope with the casualty list."

"How bad was it?" a scribe wanted to know.

"Plenty. We welcome Karnarveron back following a month of his being on the injured reserve list, just in time to lose three or four others. Arnie Jennings has a bad ankle. If he's ready for Sunday I'll be vastly surprised. Matson'll play with his hand in a cast. How much use he'll be is open to question. Andy Robertson has a concussion. He won't even be out of the hospital until Wednesday or Thursday. Hal Honegger and

Lyndon Bentley both were banged on their thigh muscles, and they're pretty sore. Yogi thinks they'll respond by the end of the week. Outside of a few little items of that nature, we're in great shape."

"Coach, do you envision problems getting your team 'up' for the Steeler game?" asked the man from the *Post*. "After all, there's likely to be a natural letdown on the heels of the tremendous performance against Dallas. And Pittsburgh *is* one-four-and-one."

Draven considered this briefly. "I'd have to say so, Stan. Mental attitude is always a headache when your team is coming off a key game and facing one that should be easier. You can bet on one thing, though. I won't let 'em forget how the Steelers took us apart at Ithaca back in August. Despite their record, they've had some miserable breaks. They could just as easily have won four. If my guys take them for patsies, they're in for a rude shock."

Draven answered questions for nearly an hour with the customary forthrightness and candor that normally characterized his relations with the press. Still and all, it was fairly obvious to those present that his mind was far away. He had a banged-up ball club, a hungry, cellar-dwelling team to face in the Steelers, and after that, crucial games with the Browns in Cleveland and the Cardinals at home. It didn't comprise, to Draven's way of thinking, a picture lending itself to optimism.

The head trainer, Yogi Di Orio, his assistants, plus Dr. Lotts, labored harder in that five-day period, Monday through Friday, than they ever had within their memory. The Giants' bills for tape, bandages, cotton balls, unguents, muscle relaxants, cortisone, novocaine, and B-12 vitamin solution mounted astronomically. Diathermy machines, whirlpool bath, and ultrasonic sound devices all stayed in constant use. Crutches and casts were common sights.

Wayne Draven and his staff toiled just as valiantly as the medical people, but at week's end the coach had the feeling he was waging an uphill fight. In practice, the Giants were sluggish, lethargic; all Draven's efforts seemed to go for naught.

When the time arrived to brief the squad on the game plan, Draven was forced to make adjustments in his original thinking both offensively and defensively. What he finally came up with wasn't to his liking in all respects, but, given the Giants' patently offhand attitude toward the Steelers and the injury situation, there was no alternative.

"First of all—offense," Draven said. "Farrell, Flood, Baxter, listen especially. There are two major areas we think we can exploit. From all reports, the Steelers had a few racked up themselves in their game against the Lions. One was Bud Healey, their strong-side cornerback. He has an ankle that's still supposed to be giving him fits. If Healey can't go, Colter will have to stick Randy Beyers in there in place of him. Beyers is highly touted, but he's only a second-year man and thus likely to make a mistake or two. Either way, we run our pass plays toward George Pyle right off the bat, particularly on deep patterns. If we give them problems back in the secondary early, I figure Colter, being a sound coach, will see to it that either Healey or Beyers gets help handling Pyle. If they start to use double coverage on him, that might leave Pell open someplace else. We'll play it by ear once we see how it goes. But no matter what, you quarterbacks keep the pressure on Healey or Beyers by firing Pyle at them to see how they react. Judge accordingly.

"That's A. Now for B—the Steelers lost Johnny Zoltan for the season at defensive left end. The swing man there, Rich Kraling, doesn't have Zoltan's lateral speed, and he can be blocked a heck of a lot more easily. That should mean our running plays to the right, on quick pitches and power sweeps, might be very effective. The same goes for our slip screen and swing passes in that direction.

"Now, to the defense. I know we're hurting, and some of you people will be playing out of position.

But try to remember what we saw in the films. Don't get complacent because Pittsburgh doesn't own too much of an offensive punch and is last in the league in scoring. Don Grant, their fullback, is back off the injured list for this game, and that'll beef up their ground attack. He's a good runner who can hurt you, especially if he turns the corner and takes off to the outside. So no matter what, if you linebackers and cornerbacks are chasing him, make every effort to head him back to the inside where there's a crowd. If he winds up out in the open with a single man to beat, he can be murder.

"Our pass defense and pass rush, I think, will be the key to any success we have against the Steelers. You must bear in mind four factors. Their quarterback, Bill Neilson, is in his second season. He had a knee operation over the winter. The offensive tackles are both relatively inexperienced. Plus—" Draven paused and broke into a smile he was far from feeling— "Honegger and Bentley assure me they'll be in top shape for the game, though Yogi Di Orio tells me their diagnoses are slightly on the optimistic side. I never try to second-guess my trainer, so I prefer to take his word for Hal's and Lyndon's condition.

"Considering the factors I just mentioned, it'll be up to the front four to get through and keep Neilson off balance. Under ordinary circumstances we'd blitz our linebackers and occasionally a safety to shake him up and pile pressure on their inexperienced tackles, but with our deep situation what it is we don't dare.

"We know most of Neilson's tendencies from the films. Be watching for them. He has a habit of throwing on first down. Likewise, he's apt to gamble on second and short. When he has third and long, nine times out of ten he'll try to hit his split end, Jackson, on a square-out to the wide side of the field. Occasionally he'll call a flood pattern left and throw to the tight end on the weak side just to cross you up. Look out for that, too. If you suspect it, Bentley, cheat a little and start moving in before the snap. In any event, don't get caught flat-footed."

There was more, much more, as Wayne Draven held his final briefing of the week. Questions were asked and answered, assignments reshuffled, plays diagrammed on the blackboard.

From all external appearances the session was a normal one in every respect. *Save for complacency,* Draven thought. *They're favored by fourteen and a half points and act as if it should be fifty. I don't like it. I've seen it happen too many times before. They're presuming the game is already in the bag, and it's only Thursday night.*

113

While preserving a tight-lipped outward appearance of optimism, by late Sunday all Wayne Draven's latent fears had been fulfilled—in spades. The Steelers put together their best afternoon of football since the preseason tilt at Ithaca, trouncing the overconfident Giants, 30 to 10. Beyers intercepted two Chips Farrell passes, setting up a touchdown and one of Pittsburgh kicker Bob Forsyte's three field goals. Bill Neilson received exceptional pass protection from his two offensive tackles, completing 16 of 28 for 211 yards and a pair of 6-pointers. The Giants, hurting at several positions due to injuries, and failing to execute well in any single department, were never in the ball game. They trailed 27–3 entering the final quarter. Indeed, had it not been for a pass interference call in the end zone that set them up on the Steeler 1-yard line, they might have suffered the ignominy of going without a touchdown.

As it turned out, things could have been worse for the Giants. At Cleveland, Dave Monroe passed 38 yards to Bill Barton in the final fifteen seconds for the score that allowed Dallas to tie the Browns, 24–24. Thus, with a 5-1-1 record, Cleveland took over first place in the Century Division by a slim half game. The Giants dropped into a tie for second with the Cardinals, who had lost to Chicago, at 5 wins, 2 losses.

The head coach reviewed the situation and found it not to his liking at all. Searching for a redeeming feature, the taciturn Draven found at least one. Half the season was now gone, and the New Yorkers still showed no long-range signs of plummeting toward the mediocre finish the writers had predicted. Nevertheless, Draven told himself as he emplaned with the team for Cleveland, it was small consolation. He wanted to win it all. He had to win. Draven was a man of fierce and awesome pride, in no sense of the word a graceful loser. The previous two dismal seasons had been real periods of torment for him, and he wasn't anxious for a repeat performance, especially with the team off to such a fine start. Finally there was the matter of his own job security; his contract would soon be due for renewal.

The Browns proved stubborn on their home field, but the Giants were able to squeeze out a 14 to 13 victory in a fumble-filled encounter played under polar weather conditions. Apparently the game Dallas had snatched away the week before rose as a psychological specter to haunt Cleveland. In addition, stung by the Pittsburgh loss and sparked by a clear shot at the Division lead, the Giant defense was superb in the face of a freak wind-whipped, snow-laden gale that poured in off Lake Erie, reducing the visibility to zero and the temperature below the freezing point.

"Considering the elements," Wayne Draven pointed out at the midweek film session, "plus the toughness of that veteran Cleveland defense, I think Chips called a well-nigh perfect game. That zone defense of theirs isn't particularly vulnerable to the long pass, which we knew before we started. They double-teamed Pyle all afternoon—one man short and the strong-side safety helping out in the deep zone. As a result they had to handle the other side man-for-man, and that left openings. We put the halfback and fullback draw on the ready list to discourage too much blitzing, and Farrell threw it in at just the right times. In the fourth quarter they were finally worried about the threat of Collins belting up the middle and were afraid to drop off too quickly. That was when Farrell found daylight in the area between the linebackers and the secondary and started tossing those medium-length passes to Pell, Jennings, and Morris.

"Result, touchdown and ball game. It was well done. But that's past history. Let's look at the Cardinal movies now."

As the NFL moved past the halfway mark in the schedule certain patterns became clearly evident in the Divisional standings. In the West, the Packers and Colts were a sure bet to battle it out for the Western

Conference title. In the East, Dallas had the Capitol Division title all but sewn up. The Century Division race, however, seemed bound to go down to the wire in a nip and tuck battle between Cleveland and New York, with St. Louis hanging furtively on the outside waiting for a break. At the moment, the Giants at 6-2 held a slim lead over Cleveland at 5-2-1. St Louis, with a 5-3 record, was only one game back in third place. One false step meant disaster for the Giants. Wayne Draven was determined there should be none.

However, a coach is merely on the sidelines during a game. He can send in plays, make adjustments, fret, fume, eat himself up inside, possibly shout at the officials, the opposition, and at times his own athletcs. Remote from the action, he is powerless to intervene, to influence those happenings not covered in the playbook, blackboard drills, or film screenings. All he can do is stoically accept fumbles, weird bounces, interceptions, inopportune penalties, and, above all else, the injury jinx.

On November fifth, as the St. Louis Cardinals invaded Yankee Stadium, the Giant head coach had this fact borne home to him with stunning force. That dreadful afternoon also marked the first of a series of unforeseen circumstances that would lead to the wildest possible consequences for young Ronnie Baxter.

The Giants won the toss and chose to receive. Lyndon Bentley took advantage of wedge blocking in front of him to run the kickoff back almost to midfield.

On the opening play from scrimmage Chips Farrell called Ed Pell's number. The halfback was to go deep on his pattern, testing the Cardinals' free safety, Len Weston, league leader in pass interceptions. In actuality Pell was merely a decoy on the play; he had been instructed to report back in the huddle what sort of coverage Weston was putting on him and whether the defensive back had entirely recovered from his muscle pull of the preceding week. According to the papers, Weston was sound and healthy, but Farrell wanted to know immediately, one way or the other. Much of Draven's strategy was based on Weston's condition.

The next play began as a simple crossover maneuver on a play-action pass, Farrell faking to Pell into the line, then pitching a medium-range bullet to George Pyle.

Retreating into the pocket, Farrell cocked his arm as if to throw deep, then sought Pyle over the middle. He saw the Cardinals' defensive tackle, "Pistol Pete" Purvis, shedding his block to the left. In trouble, Farrell danced to the right a step or two, still looking downfield where Pyle, covered momentarily, contrived to break free. Planting his feet solidly, Farrell set himself to throw. Simultaneously disaster arrived in the person of Dick Bradberry, defensive end on the side opposite Purvis.

Chips Farrell's arm was just starting on its forward arc when Bradberry belted him around the knees in a hard but strictly legal charge from the blind area. The Giant quarterback toppled, and Purvis threw 270 pounds on him, high. The football dribbled to the ground a few feet away. Whistles blew. The two Cardinal defensive men rose to their feet, congratulating each other.

Farrell did not!

Lying on his back, beating helpless fists into the unyielding November turf, his face a twisted mask of pain, Farrell flopped helplessly to and fro.

The officials called time. Wayne Draven, biting his lip, with heart suddenly sunk down to his shoes, rushed onto the field, followed closely by Dr. Lotts and Yogi Di Orio. Draven knelt by his fallen quarterback, slipped an arm under his shoulders, and eased the blue-painted helmet with its white "NY" emblem from Farrell's head.

"What is it, Chips?" Draven inquired. "Where'd you get it?"

"My—knee, Coach. As I went down, I—felt—something—give. Hurts—like the very devil."

119

His features mirroring despair, Draven stood off to one side while Dr. Lotts bent for his examination. Draven had a terrible premonition, almost a practical certainty, that Farrell's injury was serious and beyond the possibility of short-term repair under the trainer's skilled hands.

The team physician worked Farrell's stocking down. He and Yogi Di Orio moved the tight silvery material of the pants away from the knee. Gently probing, touching, feeling, Dr. Lotts shook his head. He wouldn't be sure, of course, until he viewed the X rays and consulted with his orthopedic colleagues, but he could make an educated guess. He had seen too many similar knees in the course of twenty-five years with the football Giants.

Farrell was sitting up now, staring stonily ahead with a bleak look that told its own tragic tale better than ten thousand words.

"Yogi, get the stretcher," Dr. Lotts snapped. "Alert the ambulance. We'll have Chips taken to the Emergency Room of the hospital. Put a call in for Dr. Jamieson. Tell him to meet me over there in half an hour."

Out of Farrell's hearing, Draven whispered to Lotts, "How bad, Doc? I've been around this game long enough to know nobody's going to fix Chips up

with a Band-Aid and some Mercurochrome. But how bad is it? Ligaments? Cartilage?"

Lotts nodded somberly. "Looks that way. I'm afraid everything's gone, kneecap included. When Bradberry and Purvis decked him, he went down, but the leg locked and stayed up there. He should be okay again next season. Forget about the rest of this year, though."

"Great," groaned Draven. "Now I got to go with a thirty-five-year-old and a green kid. If those newspaper hotshots picked us to finish close to the bottom *with* Farrell, where are we supposed to wind up now?"

Draven helped the trainer lift the stricken player onto the stretcher and covered him with a blanket. "Take it easy, Chips. We'll be over to see you later," he said.

"Keep on winning, Coach. I'll be pulling for you and the ball club."

Draven walked slowly back to the bench. Harry Flood and Ronnie Baxter were warming up in a hurry on the sideline. The past few years had been tough on quarterbacks in the National Football League, Draven reflected. Defenses kept getting smarter, their players bigger and more mobile. His thoughts wandered back to teams that had absorbed the big blow. Detroit. Baltimore. St. Louis. Pittsburgh. His own Giants on two prior occasions. What he had dreaded had finally come to pass. The first-string signal caller knocked out of action, lost for the last six games, counting the current one just begun. How high were the odds against it, and why had it happened to him?

Draven called Harry Flood and Ronnie Baxter to him. "I don't have to tell you guys that it's up to you now. Harry, no pep talk in the world is going to change anything. What will be, will be. You know our game plan. Follow through on it. Ronnie, never mind the phones. I want you standing by me. You'll probably play later, if Harry needs a breather."

The catastrophe that had befallen Chips Farrell put a definite damper on the Giants' spirits, as it was bound to do. Although they tried valiantly, the offensive spark was gone. It was mostly the defensive unit which kept the Giants in the game, led by middle linebacker Ron Lewis and strong safety Lyndon Bentley. Lewis blocked a punt and recovered a St. Louis fumble, contributing to a pair of Bobo Zarilla field goals. Bentley ran 67 yards with a pilfered Cardinal pass for a TD.

Directing the attack, Harry Flood showed a degree of rust from lack of actual game competition. His timing was slightly off on running plays, his passing just erratic enough to produce a ragged, sputtering offense. Farrell's backup man completed 11 of 25 for 131 yards, no touchdowns, and three interceptions—not a particularly distinguished afternoon.

Good as his word, Draven inserted Ronnie Baxter in the fourth quarter, with the Cards leading 27–13, in an effort to spark the stumbling offense. Ronnie took charge quickly, throwing seven passes, hitting on four of them for 68 yards. In addition he picked up 13 more yards with a desperation dash for daylight when apparently trapped for a loss behind the line. But it was to no avail. The listless Giants simply could not push the ball across for another score. Ronnie was satisfied with his own play, but, like the rest of the squad, was terribly disappointed with their team effort.

This Sunday seemed to be turning into a day of gloom and despair for the Giants. If losing Chips Farrell and then the game wasn't bad enough, word came through as they were heading for the dressing room that Cleveland had handily beaten the Vikings. Now their first place standing was gone, too.

The team straggled dispiritedly into the clubhouse. The players had their minor wounds attended to by Yogi Di Orio and his staff, then showered and dressed in silence. Gathering in small groups, they waited,

124

downcast, conversing in undertones. Even the writers went about their tasks more quietly than usual, sensing that no one felt much like answering questions at such a time.

At length suspicion became certainty. Yogi Di Orio entered from his training room, spoke briefly to Draven, and the two left together. In short order, the coach returned. He pushed his hat back on his head and stood in the center of the concrete floor. The Giants crowded around. They listened as Draven's unadorned speech closed the door to any lingering hopes of a medical miracle.

"Dr. Lotts just called from the hospital," said Draven. "His diagnosis has been confirmed. Chips Farrell's knee is in bad shape. Throwing out all the excess verbiage, the ligaments are torn and the kneecap cracked. Dr. Jamieson is operating on him Tuesday morning. Jamieson's off-the-cuff opinion is that Chips ought to be okay by the time we open camp in Fairfield next July.

"That's about the size of it. I'll leave you with your own thoughts about today, and I'll see you Tuesday. I imagine the Steelers will be licking their chops all week, waiting to get a crack at us without Farrell. They'll be putting plenty of pressure on Harry Flood Sunday. We're going to figure ways and means of taking some of the heat off. One last word. Don't allow what has happened to Farrell to psych you for the rest of the season like it did today. Other teams have survived the loss of important personnel. So will we."

Shoulders hunched deep into his topcoat collar against the insistent tug of a biting wind, Ronnie walked with Bruiser Kinarski toward the subway. Each sunk in his own somber thoughts, neither wanted the other to know just how deeply the crippling injury to Chips Farrell had affected him.

Finally Kinarski turned to Ronnie. "Like the coach said, roomie, it isn't the end of the world. Harry's no youngster, but he knows how to handle himself out there. We'll be okay. Somewhere along the line Cleveland is bound to lose another game or two. And we still get one more crack at them before the end of the season."

"The natural optimism of youth," Ronnie replied, managing a weak smile. "I'm the same age as you, and I sure don't feel it. It's tough enough to win in this league when your team is in one piece. I told Draven once I wouldn't step into his shoes for all the gold in Fort Knox. I meant it then, and I mean it even more now."

"I'm with you, Ronnie. We may go out and take a few lumps fourteen Sundays in a row, but the coach gets his twelve months of the year. They nail his hide to the wall in the stands, the papers, and the front office if he doesn't win. Yet nobody stops to figure that he can't block out a defensive right tackle and left end to keep Chips whole. It's got to be the unfairest system in the world."

"You know the old saying, Bruiser. 'There are only two kinds of football coaches—those who have been fired and those who will be.' They walk into their jobs with their eyes wide open, I suppose. At least, they should."

Kinarski shrugged. "Still and all, now that Chips is hurt it may work to your advantage. You'll probably play a little more often. Harry's at an age where he has to be spelled from time to time."

"Even if it's true, don't remind me of it," Ronnie said, glaring at Kinarski. "Outside of anything else, in case you forgot it, there's a heck of a lot of extra cash at stake. We're pros, and that's the name of the game. No, much as I'd like to further my own career, I'd rather look forward to handling the phones the rest of this season and have Chips on the field running the ball club. He was money in the bank to us."

Unwittingly Ronnie Baxter had expressed an

opinion shared, without doubt, by all forty men on the Giants' roster. Personally and financially, the good right arm and shrewd play-calling of Chips Farrell would be sorely missed.

10 | *Run to the Wire*

THE NEXT DAY the papers screamed, "FARRELL LOST FOR SEASON!"

With only minor variations, the New York dailies trumpeted the sad tidings in bold headlines on their sports pages. Each columnist attempted to analyze the situation and then went on to speculate what moves the Giants might make to bolster their quarterbacking corps.

In the *Times*, Art Daugherty wrote: "NFL rules forbid interleague movement of players by trade or sale after the seventh week of the season. Hence, since the tenth week is at hand, any such avenue of assistance that might have been open to the Giants is automatically closed. Actually it may be just as well. It is a known fact that the best deals in sports accrue

129

to a team trading from strength. This the Giants certainly would not have been able to claim. They still cling to second place, in defiance of all gravitational laws. Other NFL outfits with a spare quarterback available (especially those having an outside shot at the title, or even Play-Off participation) would either flatly refuse to talk business or demand half the New York ball club in return.

"While it is true Harry Flood has been languishing on the Giant bench for the better part of the last four seasons and is approaching venerable status for a professional athlete, there can be no dispute that he is a basically sound quarterback. After Sunday it remains to be seen whether the New Yorkers can win with him at the helm on a regular basis. However, from this vantage point it seems they might do considerably worse than simply sticking with Flood the last five games. Indeed, what other solution is there?

"In any evaluation of the position in which the injury to Chips Farrell has left the Giants, one other factor must not be overlooked. Young Ronnie Baxter, the rookie phenom from Tulsa, has up to now been brought along slowly by Wayne Draven. He has been inserted in games already safely won or hopelessly lost. In brief appearances he has looked good and bad by turns, which is only to be expected of a first-year man.

With an aging Harry Flood asked to go full time, Draven may not be able much longer to handpick Baxter's spots for him. Ronnie could be forced to mature in a hurry. It's a tough way to grow up in a league which places such a high premium on experience. But, in our humble opinion, he should be able to handle it. This Ronnie Baxter is one quarterback in the making who has an exceedingly bright future ahead of him."

Larry Conwell, in his *Daily News* piece, attacked the problem from a slightly different angle.

"The Giants," Conwell wrote, "have suffered a grievous loss with Chips Farrell out for the year. The Century Division race, as expected, is going down to the wire in a three-team fight. Cleveland, at 6-2-1, leads the pack. Draven's Dragoons hang tight at their heels at 6-3, with the Cards at 6-3 hanging just as tightly.

"However, as the former Governor of New York, the late Al Smith, once said, 'Let's look at the record.' In this case it takes the form of the remaining schedule, which favors the Giants while militating against the chances of Cleveland. The Giants finish, in order, with the Steelers in Pittsburgh; Green Bay, Chicago, and Cleveland at Yankee Stadium; and Detroit away. The Browns, on the other hand, face three of their last five opponents on enemy soil, one of which is Green Bay at Lambeau Field. It should be a tough row to hoe for them.

"Our premise is this: While the Giants, according to league rules, cannot obtain a quarterback from any of the other clubs—even if the latter were disposed to deal with them—they may not be as badly off as the alarmists moan they are. Harry Flood has proved before that he can do the job, when he played regularly for several seasons in the Canadian Football League with the Calgary Stampeders. Perhaps he doesn't have all the equipment of a Chips Farrell, yet eleven years of pro experience certainly can't be discounted.

"In addition the Giants are fortunate in having carried three quarterbacks this campaign instead of an extra tackle or linebacker. It was a luxury they felt they could afford, their veteran defensive situation being what it was. Ron Baxter, the talented newcomer from Tulsa, may see considerable action before the last whistle is blown December 17. He has shown well in brief stints, and it's a known fact Wayne Draven and Giant brass are high on him. With the kind of dough they shelled out to induce him to sign, how can they be anything else?

"Along the sports beat one hears names bandied

about. Speculation is rife as to possible New York moves. The reactivation of Ben Barton, taxi-squad quarterback. Coaxing Sammy Foreman, at age thirty-eight going on fifty, out of retirement. Et cetera, et cetera. If you hear any of these things, our advice is forget 'em. Wayne Draven must win or lose with Flood and Baxter because there is no reasonable alternative. We predict the Giants and Browns will thunder neck and neck down to the wire. In any event, the two clash on December 10 here in New York. All the marbles may be waiting to be picked up then."

At the Quarterback Club luncheon the same day an outwardly affable Wayne Draven refused to push the panic button.

"You guys are all trying to read something into this situation that simply isn't present," he told the writers. "I'll just refresh your memory a little. One year a certain NFL team came within a disputed field goal of winning the championship. They had lost not one but two quarterbacks. The player they wound up with finally hadn't played the position since college, five years earlier. My Giants are like an octopus. You cut off one arm, and there are still seven pretty good ones left. Ball control and defense, those are the keys right now. You have those working well for you, plus better execution of fundamentals than the other fellow, and you're going to win no matter who's calling the signals. Somewhere along the line, you ink-stained characters have taken the notion into your heads that Harry Flood is about to be struck down by the Old Man with the Scythe. I call your attention to two people well into their forties doing very well for Cleveland and Houston. Let's leave it at that, shall we?"

On Sunday, November twelfth, the Giants were at Pittsburgh. Cleveland journeyed to Franklin Field for a game against the Eagles.

Luck is a capricious lady. There is seemingly no pattern to her selections. If she takes away, at times she can also choose to give.

The Steelers had already defeated New York twice; with less than two minutes left to play they apparently were on their way to a third upset triumph, leading 17 to 16. The Giant offense, to put it bluntly, had sputtered badly. Harry Flood threw one TD pass to Arnie Jennings from 11 yards out. Bobo Zarilla booted field goals of 33, 27, and 19 yards. Ronnie Baxter, in two turns at the throttle, had done nothing noteworthy.

The scoreboard clock showed one forty-five remaining. On their own 15, the Steelers faced a third-and-10 situation. Pitt quarterback Bill Neilson, desperately trying to retain possession of the ball, dropped back to pass. The Giants had read his intentions correctly. Everyone was coming in on the blitz, including safety Hal Honegger. In the late afternoon shadows, where the overhang of the banked stadium tiers broke the sun's slants near the goal line, a blue and white number 27, Honegger, covered Neilson like a tent back on the Steeler 7. The Giants immediately called a time-out.

With one twenty-five left, Pittsburgh's punter, Ted Van Buren, stood hands outstretched, feet firmly planted a yard or so from the back line of the end zone.

The center snap was a poor one, coming to Van Buren on the bounce. He juggled it for a split second, then strode forward and dropped the ball toward his upswinging toe. Al Waskoff, the Giants' defensive right end, having gotten a fine initial charge, found a bit of a chink in the Steelers' front wall armor. Rushing through, he was just too late to effect the block he wanted so much.

Nonetheless, his mere presence that close to the kicker destroyed the startled, hurried Van Buren's timing. Instead of meeting the pigskin solidly, he slithered the boot off the side of his foot at an angle to the left. The ball started to rise, but didn't carry very far. Its flight barred by the goalposts, it struck the right-hand upright, caromed away, bounced crazily on the ground, and rolled out of the end zone. As the crowd sat stunned by the totally unexpected turn of events, two officials rushed up, hands held over their heads, palms touching. It was, of course, an automatic safety. With a minute left, the Giants had taken the lead at 18 to 17!

Following their recovery of an onside free kick attempt by the Steelers after the score, the Giants ran two cautious line plunges and ate up the clock. Some of their jubilation was tempered, though, when they learned from Yogi Di Orio's transistor radio in the clubhouse that Cleveland and St. Louis had also won, thus maintaining the status quo.

On the nineteenth, the formidable Green Bay Packers invaded Yankee Stadium. The Pack seemed to have everything going for them: superb confidence born of several recent championships; cool, precise teamwork and almost technically perfect play; the tough and canny coaching of Vic Costello; and finally the field leadership of Bill Crimmins. All this was often enough to defeat an opponent before the game started. Wayne Draven recognized this psychological advantage the Packers carried with them, and was determined that it would not affect his team. Starting on the first day of practice the week before tho game, Draven and his assistants snarled this slogan at their charges: "The Packers can be beaten, and you are the guys that can do it!"

By late Sunday afternoon the Giants had proven their coach right. They toppled the mighty Packers, and at their own game—ball control. It was one of those days when everything clicked for the Giants. They took the kickoff, then marched 80 yards in nine plays for the touchdown. Given a lift by this early score, the Giants managed to keep possession of the ball most of the afternoon, scoring another TD in the second quarter and a field goal in the third. The Packer offense never got off the ground until the fourth quarter, and by then it was too late. The Giants managed to hang on in the face of the resurgent Packer attack, winning 17–14.

Although they kept winning, and their record had risen to an excellent 8-3, the strain and tension of the grueling campaign was beginning to tell on the Giants. They could neither overhaul Cleveland, 8-2-1, nor shake St. Louis, 8-3. Collectively they felt like a man on a treadmill, constantly forced to run harder and harder just to stay in the same place. It was discouraging, disheartening, almost futile, they thought. They had put forth their best efforts, overcome the loss of Chips Farrell, been blessed by the most outrageously bizarre stroke of fortune at Pittsburgh, and beaten the

Packers. And to what end? Second place still, the squad told themselves with ever-growing annoyance. Would the Cardinals and Browns never falter? Could they expect no help from the other members of the NFL?

Nerves tightened and tempers frayed. As the season swung into its final three weeks, the pressure mounted and manifested itself in a dozen small, yet explicit ways. Previously unimportant incidents grew into disasters of major proportion. Teammates snapped at each other, and on more than one occasion at newsmen. Several of the Giants petitioned their coach to bar a certain writer from the dressing room, only to be curtly told that such an action was against league policy. Wayne Draven was forced to levy a couple of fines, which brought on more grumbling.

Even Ronnie Baxter found himself involuntarily involved in the war of pressure the team was fighting. All season long he had walked the narrow, precarious line between the relative self-effacement expected of a first-year man and the easy confidence a college All-American should display. He had stoically borne the practical jokes and the mild hazing, viewing them as customary components of a pro football education. He had politely said "Yes, sir" and "No, sir" to one and all in the beginning, and he had deferred to those he considered rated it by reason of seniority and greater knowledge.

On a particular midweek morning, with the squad viewing Chicago movies, Ronnie was seated in front of Jim Karnarveron, the huge All-Pro defensive tackle the last three years. The "Buddha" liked to smoke cigars, and it was agreed unanimously that their quality left much to be desired. From time to time Karnarveron erupted a mouthful of foul-smelling smoke which invariably wreathed Ronnie's head.

The latter stood it as long as he was able, then turned and whispered, "Jim, will you for heaven's sake put that thing out? I'm about to suffocate."

Karnarveron remained unperturbed. "If you don't care for my cigar, Ronnie, I'd suggest you change your chair," he replied mildly. Despite his hulking frame, there wasn't an aggressive or hostile bone in Karnarveron's body, except on the football field.

All of Ronnie's irritations, frustrations, annoyances, and fears suddenly boiled over in anger. He knew it was childish and stupid, a veritable tempest in a teapot. Yet unaccountably, in the same manner as so many tiny things of the past few days had quickly mushroomed into larger ones, Ronnie allowed a simple happening to get completely out of hand.

Jumping up, he yelled, "No, I won't either! *You*

move, you big ox! All season long I've had to put up with that chemical warfare from you, and I'm sick and tired of it! It's a wonder I've got any lungs left."

"Calm down, Ron, calm down," said Karnarveron, a hazy shadow in the darkened room.

Wayne Draven snapped on the lights and strode down the aisle, face black with the rage he felt inside. He swung on Ronnie, demanding an explanation.

"Coach, Jim here refused to quit blowing that miserable cigar smoke at me while the films were on. I couldn't even breathe."

"I did not!" Karnarveron flared.

"Now cut this out!" Draven said sharply. "You're both supposed to be professional football players, not a couple of ten-year-olds."

Ronnie refused to be mollified. He placed a finger against Karnarveron's chest, prodding. "I've had just about as much of you as I can take, big shot. Let's go someplace and settle this right now, once and for all. You and me. Alone."

As if an unseen hand had flipped a switch, laughter swept the room. The very thought of Ronnie Baxter engaging the six-eight, 290-pound tackle in hand-to-hand combat was totally, outlandishly ludicrous. No sooner had the words left his mouth than Ronnie realized that very fact. Most of all, he became aware

140

of how errantly foolish his entire course of action had been. Ronnie hated pop-offs, and here he was, he thought, being one himself for no good reason!

Chagrined, he smiled, shaking his head. He addressed Draven. "I apologize, Coach. My fault. I could have moved, like Jim said. Silly to let such a piddling little incident bug me. Anyway, I don't really have any yen to tangle with Buddha. My old pappy told me a long time ago never to pick on somebody that wasn't my size—either way." He stuck out a hand. Karnarveron engulfed it, also grinning now.

In a jiffy, sensing that the affair had cooled down, Draven decided to forget the matter without further ado. In thirty years he had seen a hundred similar short-lived flare-ups, even a few genuine fistfights, that had served to clear the air and release accumulated pressures. The coach knew how difficult it was for players to be in contention for a title, especially when the days grew short and every game counted for so much. The winner's share in a title tilt, with the added revenues of a berth in the Super Bowl game, could equal or better a man's salary for the whole season.

Draven reflected as he threaded his way back toward the projector that there was another angle that ought not to be overlooked. Ronnie Baxter's outburst might serve a useful secondary purpose by taking some of the crushing weight off a youthful pair of shoulders. A rookie's life wasn't any bed of roses under optimum circumstances, especially for a newcomer who arrived highly touted. And to a quiet, decent kid like Ronnie, who worried constantly that he wasn't contributing enough, yet saw the numerous, obvious errors he made when he did play—well, it was good for him to blow off steam once in a while. It indicated to Draven that Ronnie was perhaps ready to shed some of the shell he had molded around himself and join the group in the truest sense.

Before he extinguished the lights again, Draven had his final say on the subject.

"I don't mind you prima donnas having a spat now and then, but I do kind of wish you'd save your energy for the opposition—in this case, the Chicago Bears. Okay. Shall we start one more time to find out what makes them tick offensively?"

11 | *Reprieve*

THE CHICAGO Bears were a so-so, in-and-out, hot-and-cold team with a mediocre 5-6 record. They had a long list of problems, including a sputtering offense, a linebacking corps decimated by injuries and retirements, and a quarterback whose mobility was limited due to a chronically bad knee. It should have been an easy game for the Giants, favored by 13½ points, that Sunday, December third.

As it turned out it was just that—in the wrong direction. Red Bekins, the Bears' signal caller, got practically no pass rush from the New York front four and threw at his leisure most of the afternoon. This placed an intolerable burden on the Giants' secondary, which proved unequal to the task. Bekins unloaded four touchdown passes. In addition he set up a field goal when he caught the Giants in one of their few successful blitzes and sent his big, fast halfback, George Soames, pouring up the middle for 37 yards. Chicago led at the half, 24 to 3, and the handwriting was up on the wall early.

In the locker room at intermission, Wayne Draven adjusted, pleaded, chewed out, but once again had the distinct feeling it was no use. He knew his squad, as it had been against the Steelers earlier, was simply unenthusiastic about the game and was unable to work itself into the fever-pitch mental attitude required to play winning football.

"Maybe it's the strain of a long season beginning to tell. Maybe you're looking ahead to Cleveland. Maybe a lot of things," Draven told his players. "Whatever the reason, this is a different ball club today. You aren't prepared. You're making stupid mistakes. Worst of all is the pass rush—or lack of it. Well, try this little number on for size. If these jokers beat you, it won't make a great deal of difference what you do against the Browns, except possibly nailing down third place. If you have any professional pride at all get out there now and do the job you're capable of."

Draven's tongue-lashing was of little avail. The Giants' defensive unit improved somewhat in the second half, managing to hold the Bears to 10 points.

However, the offense failed really to find itself. Harry Flood and Ronnie Baxter threw 46 times, completing 18, each accounting for a scoring pass. On the other hand, their passes were intercepted on four occasions; once Ronnie coughed up the leather on a costly fumble inside the Bears' 15. The final gun exploded with Chicago the surprise 34–17 winners.

It was a weary, disconsolate band of Giants who dispiritedly dragged themselves off the Yankee Stadium gridiron into the clubhouse. Hating themselves for their lackluster performance, feeling to a man they had blown an entire season in one miserable game, they automatically peeled off uniforms, stripped away layers of tape, and sat on stools before cubicles in grimy, uncaring nudity. Nobody said very much; gloom hung in the silence like a thick London fog. Each player reviewed his personal sins of omission and commission on the field. Some smoked. Others lifted soft drink bottles to their mouths.

Then the writers, their play-by-play stories having been filed, stole in for the inevitable postgame postmortem. They converged first on Wayne Draven.

"Tough one, Wayne," said Art Daugherty of the *Times* in a sympathetic voice. He had been in the business long enough to know that any coach is in a homicidal mood after a shellacking, especially by a team which didn't figure to win. Draven was no exception. There were times when Daugherty felt he would rather walk into a cage with a man-eating lion than approach Draven following a loss. This was one of them.

"Yeah. Sure. Thanks." Draven's reply came in one-word bursts, punctuated by the scraping of his cleats against the concrete floor.

"There's a small consolation, though. The Packers are manhandling the Cards at Green Bay. Old Number Fifteen went nuts today. Three TD's in the first quarter. I think he's making up for last week. It was twenty-eight to seven at the half."

Draven looked up. "That helps some, for sure. Anybody hear a final on the Browns-Vikings thing? The Browns were ahead ten to nothing last word we had. I expect it's a lot worse now."

Yogi Di Orio tore out of the training room, holding his transistor radio aloft. "Listen to this, you guys," he yelled. "We still got a chance. I just heard a third period score, which must be old by now. The Browns and Vikings were tied ten to ten going into the final quarter!"

A ragged cheer went up from the Giants, for suddenly there appeared a slender ray of hope. If the Cards lost, as they were well on their way to doing, and the Vikings could also pull off a miracle, then, as Yogi said, there still remained a chance. Maybe they hadn't butchered it after all!

"Good grief!" Draven groaned, smiting his forehead. "I clean forgot! Lenny Meyers is scouting the Browns for us in Minneapolis. Let me at that phone, boys! I'll put in a call to the press box there and see if they're finished yet!"

Draven rushed to the pay phone on the wall, shouting, "Round up all the quarters you can find!" He inserted a dime, gave the information to a long-distance operator, waited a moment or two, dropped in coins, listened, then spoke into the mouthpiece.

"Lenny? Wayne Draven in New York. Yeah, we lost. How's it going where you are?"

He turned to face a suddenly rapt audience. "Cleveland is leading, thirteen to ten. Naz Chalakian just booted a twenty-seven yard field goal." A chorus of disappointment resounded in the humid, steamy atmosphere. "Lenny, hang on the phone until it's over. Tell me what's happening, and I'll relay the info here.

"Browns' kickoff went out through the end zone. It's the Vikings' ball, first and ten on the twenty, with exactly three and a half minutes to go."

The Vikings' quarterback, Packenham, faced with a Cleveland prevent defense that included the standard three-man rush and an extra defender deep, methodically went to work. Knowing that the Vikings would have to take to the air to conserve time, willing to concede short gains in order not to allow completion of the "home run" toss, the Browns left a couple of tiny openings.

Throwing sideliners, occasionally sending a running back on a play that terminated out-of-bounds, and scrambling as little as possible to save time, Packenham guided his team to a first down on the Cleveland 11. The excited press around Draven was practically smothering him. Sweat poured in rivulets off his face and dripped unheeded from his chin. He was forced finally to hold up a hand for quiet.

"There's one-forty on the clock, Lenny says. Plenty of time yet. Come on, you Vikings! Take it in! Okay, they're set. Packenham fakes to the fullback driving up the middle. He's bootlegging the ball to the right. He's being chased. He's throwing now. It's into the end zone. Touchdown! Touchdown! To Kemmerer, his tight end!"

A jubilant clamor of sheer animal joy assaulted the dressing room rafters. Jim Karnarveron lifted Ronnie up, almost crushing his ribs, and danced around with him. Harry Flood poured a full bottle of Coke over Bull Durham's head. Yogi Di Orio was somehow thrust

into a shower, fully clothed; he presently emerged, grinning, resembling a dripping Labrador retriever.

"We got a big break there," Wayne Draven was saying. "The Cleveland strong-side safety slipped and fell. Kemmerer and Palmer ran crossover patterns."

The Vikings scored again on the last play of the game, after having intercepted a desperation pass at the Cleveland 28. So, with St. Louis smothered 45–21 by Green Bay, and Minnesota upending the Browns 24–13, the Giants were still alive!

The Century Division race, to no one's surprise, stayed a tight three-team battle. To that point, Cleveland had won 8, lost 3, and tied 1. New York and St. Louis hung close at 8-4.

It was a radically different, uplifted Giant crew that left the Stadium dressing room.

Wayne Draven fired a last parting shot, calling them all together for a moment.

"I won't keep you long," drawled the coach. "I know your wives and girl friends are waiting for you, and tomorrow is free time. Just let me say this. You played lousy football today. You lost, as you should have. In spite of it, you got a reprieve. We stay in the thick of it, although ours may be the hardest of the three tasks among the top teams. Cleveland plays us here, then winds up with the Steelers in Pittsburgh. We tackle the Browns next week, followed by the Lions in Detroit.

"Somebody Up There has seen fit to throw a break our way. Does a single member of this organization believe now that we can go on and take it all?"

The concerted cheer that echoed and reechoed up to the ceiling and bounced off the walls sent a thrill of pride through Draven. He knew he had been rough on them; brutally, impossibly rough on occasions. He had chided them, derided them, made sarcastic remarks, enforced discipline by fines and threats when necessary. In his favor, Draven thought, he had counseled, cajoled, applied psychology, and listened to complaints real and fancied.

He had taken this team farther than it had any right to go. Now the rest was up to them.

While Draven knew that money was the prime motivation for professional athletes in any sport, it was evident the Giants had a considerable amount of gung-ho about them, too. The dollar sign wasn't the be-all and end-all of their collective existence. Individual and team desire remained the major ingredients of victory.

The coach walked somberly to his car in the Stadium parking lot. Looking skyward in the frosty night, he suddenly saw a meteor streak across the heavens, leaving a glittering trail in its wake.

Could it be an omen? Draven wondered. Was it really in the cards for his Giants to beat Cleveland and then Dallas in the play-off?

12 | *"Bring on the Cowboys!"*

ALL THE EXCITEMENT of the entire season seemed to be concentrated in that next-to-last Sunday of the regular football schedule. Everyone knew that the impossibly tight Century Division race was going to break wide open. The question was: Where would the pieces fall?

As it turned out, the Giants picked up all the marbles that Sunday, including the Division lead and a shot at Dallas for the Conference title. It may have been that the loss of Chips Farrell drove the Giants against the Browns. The loss of their quarterback and the struggle they had made all season against fierce odds had given the team a fine *esprit de corps,* a tough togetherness. The Giants went out on the field united behind Harry Flood, grimly determined to take the

153

elusive lead away from the Browns.

It worked. But it was a hard, bitter, grinding struggle all the way. The Browns were just as determined to keep their lead as the Giants were to take it away from them, and at half time the score was deadlocked at 14–14. The score remained that way until the final quarter, when the Browns, capitalizing on a Giant fumble, were able to add a field goal, taking the lead, 17–14.

With a ferocity born of desperation the Giants battled back. After taking the kickoff, the New Yorkers ground out 70 yards in eleven plays, taking the ball to a first down on the Cleveland 10 and eating up great chunks of the clock. Then the Cleveland defense stiffened, and New York was left with third and goal on the Browns' 8 with one minute remaining.

A deathlike silence reigned in the stadium as Harry Flood crouched behind the center. He took the snap and backpedaled furiously as the Cleveland rush poured in on him. At the last moment, before he was buried by Cleveland defenders, Flood flipped a short screen pass to Collins, who was waiting in the flat. Behind good blocking, and with great second effort, Collins plunged into the end zone, carrying several Browns with him. The stands erupted with a roar of approval. The more enthusiastic fans were already pouring onto

154

the field, and soon the sidelines were black with humanity. Another roar arose when the extra point sailed through the uprights.

The Browns tried, but the spark was gone from their offense and time was rapidly running out. The final gun found them, still battling, with a first down on the Giant 40.

Wayne Draven started toward the Cleveland coach to shake hands, but he never made it. He was swarmed upon by ecstatic fans and players, and carried bodily into the clubhouse. There, pandemonium reigned. Word had come through that Dallas was roundly thumping St. Louis. New York stood alone atop the Century Division with a 9-4 record, and only the lowly Detroit Lions remained between them and the Conference title tilt with Dallas. "Bring on the Cowboys!" resounded through the locker room.

However, the following Sunday the "lowly" Lions proved almost too much for the overconfident Giants. The Lions, with nothing to lose and relishing the spoiler's role, came roaring out of their den in Tiger Stadium to completely outplay the listless New Yorkers in the first half. The 17–0 score on the scoreboard at half time was enough to scare some life into the Giants. They came back with two quick touchdowns in the third quarter and two field goals in the fourth, winning

20–17. Altogether it was a harrowing day for the Giant fans, the team, and especially Wayne Draven. But no matter how the game had gone in Detroit, they had won and were returning to New York, tired but happy, with the Century Division title in their pockets.

Wayne Draven had one last word for them before they got off the plane. "I want to congratulate you on performing a small miracle this season. I thought you could do it all along, but sometimes this title we clinched today seemed pretty far away. You'd like a nice long rest now. Don't count on it. We've got Dallas ahead of us for the Eastern Conference title, then the NFL Championship, and then the Super Bowl. I intend to have this team play in, and win, each of those games. Dallas is a start, and I don't have to tell you how much is riding on this game. Nor do I have to tell you how tough they are. All I can say is, be prepared— both mentally and physically. That's all." Draven put his hat on and watched his team file silently out of the plane and down the ramp. *Could they really bring it off?* he wondered as he collected his coat and papers and followed them.

13 | *Black Friday*

THAT NEXT WEEK, with quiet, grim determination that effectively hid the turmoil churning inside them, Wayne Draven and his assistants prepared for the payoff meeting. The Giants had come off the Detroit game in reasonably good physical condition, with the exception of starting offensive tackle Don Payson, who had a pulled thigh muscle. However, Yogi Di Orio was optimistic that diathermy plus a light schedule during the week would have him ready to go by Sunday.

Even for seasoned pros, the days that followed contained a heady air of expectancy, watchful waiting, and just plain, old-fashioned hard work. Well aware of the amount of prestige and money riding on the sixty minutes of football they would play in the Cotton

Bowl, they all labored to hone to razor-sharp perfection the diverse elements of both offense and defense.

Ronnie Baxter shared the load equally with Harry Flood, alternating during signal drills and padless dummy scrimmage. The fledgling quarterback knew in his heart that, barring some unforeseen factor, he wouldn't play a single minute. He accepted this premise with tranquility, since he admitted Draven had to stand or fall on the experience Harry Flood represented.

Nonetheless, struggling to perfect his timing and judgment, remembering the Dallas defenses he had seen in their first meeting, and trying to put himself with each play call under real game conditions, Ronnie was deeply anxious to be ready—just in case. Farrell, limping around on cast and crutches, sat in on all the practice sessions, lending an able hand with the two remaining Giant quarterbacks.

Wayne Draven's game plan contained nothing new or startling, with one possible exception. It was based on what was already known of the Cowboys, plus scouting reports and films of the contests they had played since their 17–9 loss at the hands of the Giants back on October fifteenth.

"Just so you won't forget it, boys," Draven told the assembled squad, "this Dallas outfit has been one of the most consistent in the league over the past season and a half. We caught them on an off-day. It happened to be the only occasion in a span of sixteen outings when they didn't score a touchdown. We certainly can't expect that again.

"The offense that Dave Monroe runs is possibly the most varied in pro football. You'll see every set in the books and then some. Double wing, triple wing, I formation, backs in motion to the strong side, same for the weak side—everything. They're about the toughest team in the NFL to plan defenses for, but we've got to do it.

"And don't anticipate any help from *their* defense. You won't get it. That big number seventy-four, Watson, is right now two hundred and fifty-five pounds of just about the best tackle in the circuit. He's come on fast in the last month and is a cinch for All-Pro. As a unit, Dallas has held opponents to only two hundred and twenty-eight yards a game—a mere seventy-one on the ground. Enemy quarterbacks have been dumped on their duffs for losses forty-six times and have completed a shade less than forty-four percent of their passes against Dallas. I know I'm throwing a lot of figures at you, but I want to impress you with how tough this bunch can be—and is.

"So, to sum up, they've got good balance. Monroe

can fire long or short, and he'll hurt you both ways. Parsons and Waters run well and are excellent deep receivers. Their coach, Blackie Collison, is young and imaginative, altogether one of the brainiest football minds I've ever run into. I should know, because he played for me in the fifties. To give you one small example of how shrewd he is, take the Steeler game, which we'll watch on the projector in a few minutes. Pittsburgh got the bright idea that if they double-teamed Watson, they'd cut down on the Cowboys' pass rush and give Neilson more time to throw. It worked fine for a while until Collison sent an outside linebacker and Art Jurgens from the middle looping in on repeated blitzes. Soon the Steelers found they couldn't afford the luxury of double-teaming Watson. So what happened? They put one man on him, and he spent the remainder of the afternoon in the Steeler backfield."

A major cornerstone of Wayne Draven's coaching structure was to keep things relatively simple. Involved and complicated though modern professional football might be, Draven was of the opinion that most mentors outsmarted themselves in attempting to force-feed their athletes more information than they could usefully digest from week to week.

"In a nutshell, on offense we'll start out doing exactly

what we aren't supposed to do—we'll try to run the ball, control it, keep our hands on it as long as possible. Especially sweeps and deep pitchouts to spread them out a little. Counter traps up the middle, to make Mr. Watson and his three comrades up front a little wary. We'll have the halfback option pass on the ready list, number one priority, because if Dallas has a defensive weakness it's comparative lack of speed in the deep secondary.

"So far as passing is concerned, we'll play it conservatively at the start and lay off the long bomb. In other words, use the short stuff—flares, look-ins, slants, hooks. Above all—and I'll say it again—I stress ball control and avoidance of mistakes. The longer we can hold on to that football, the better off we'll be. You give these guys an inch in good field position, and they'll take three miles. In that respect, they're the Green Bay Packers of the East."

Halting his nervous pacing for a few seconds to light a cigarette, Draven returned to the task at hand.

"On defense I've no reason to change what we did against them earlier. Double coverage on Barton, cornerback and strong-side safety deep. That'll mean man-to-man coverage elsewhere, and it had better be sharp. At any cost, defensive unit, delay a split second before committing yourselves on some of their running plays, particularly that fullback dive series you handled so well last time, plus their man in motion to the strong side and run to the weak side. If you get caught leaning the wrong way they'll murder you. Keep pressure on Monroe up front—relentless pressure. Force him out of that pocket to the outside. We know he isn't nearly so effective a thrower when he's scrambling. Now, another thing. . . ."

Draven drove into further technicalities of the game plan. When he was finished, each man, having taken notes, possessed a clear mental picture of what his job would be in a given situation. After that came the specific films illustrating the points the coaches had made, the inevitable *x*'s and *o*'s on the blackboard as plays were diagrammed, lengthy talks from the staff assistants, each holding forth on his own specialty, and finally a question-and-answer session.

Ronnie Baxter never ceased to be amazed at Draven's pregame briefings. He didn't attempt to downgrade the methods of his Tulsa coach, Charley Tubbs. It was simply that Draven did so much more in so much less time. This, Ronnie admitted admiringly, constituted precision—the distillation of thirty years' know-how into a fact-crammed hour or two. And all this while fully conversant with the coaching profession's cruelest aspect: If the team won, the athletes received the credit; if it lost, the mantle of blame inevitably fell on Draven's shoulders alone. More than ever, since Chips Farrell's injury and his own flare-up with Jim Karnarveron, Ronnie had a sense of belonging he never would have thought possible at Fairfield. Could it be the result of his slowly developing maturity as a pro? A slight mellowing on the part of Draven? Or some of both?

Friday, December twenty-second dawned clear and cold in the New York area. Singly, by twos, in groups of three and four, the Giants arrived at Yankee Stadium for their final tune-up prior to emplaning for Dallas. Ronnie Baxter and Bruiser Kinarski walked in together, surveying the now familiar scene. By degrees, the dressing room was filling up, although it was yet early.

Jim Karnarveron, smoking the inevitable long black cigar, sat half-naked on a bench, reading the *News*. Chips Farrell, his right leg propped up, was playing gin rummy with George Pyle, the acknowledged club champ. Willie Collins fastidiously removed his snappy alligator loafers, placed shoe trees in them and deposited them on the floor of his cubicle. Arnie Jennings, who detested getting up in the morning, lounged yawning against the farther wall, drinking coffee from a container Yogi Di Orio had brought

him. Hal Honegger and Lyndon Bentley, the two safeties, had their heads close, arguing some obscure point
of defensive play.

Ronnie started to undress. "How're you feeling today, roomie?" he asked Bruiser Kinarski.

"Keyed up, man, keyed up," was the frank response.
"If I was any higher, my feet wouldn't be touching
the ground. I bet I could fly to Dallas without using
an airplane."

"No kidding? That's funny. I'm as calm as anything.
What's to get excited about? Don't people play for the
title every Sunday?"

Stooping down to strip off his socks, Ronnie laughed.
The exaggerated display of cool was merely camou-
flage. He knew it, and he knew his roommate did, too.
Underneath it all the young quarterback was building
to a peak of tightness such as he had never experienced
in either high school or college. He realized now that
most of the stories he had read before joining the
Giants were totally false, highly fictional accounts.
Ronnie recalled some of them. What had they said?
Old pros, steel-nerved professional athletes. Non-
worriers. Just a job to be done, like any other.

Ha! Had he not seen with his own eyes a 250-
pounder, Jack Strawbridge, become violently ill
before almost every opening whistle?—Chips Farrell

so wrought up he couldn't eat his pregame meal? Had he not heard countless tales of sleepless nights, of wives who drove players to the Stadium because the men were too upset to handle the car themselves? What a great percentage of the writers overlooked, Ronnie thought, was that pros or not, they were people, human beings, with the same emotions, fears, and doubts as laborers, shoe clerks, or bank presidents.

"Hey, Ron," tight end Frank Morris, his left-hand neighbor, said suddenly, "why's the coach so glum this morning? You'd think he'd lost his last friend."

Ronnie swiveled his head. Wayne Draven had just entered, and he did indeed seem to be extraordinarily preoccupied. He slowly traversed the room, and it was apparent he was seeking something.

Or someone.

Puzzled, Ronnie tried to figure out Draven's problem, something beyond the normal worries nagging at a coach whose team was forty-eight hours away from playing for a conference title. He shrugged.

"I don't know, Frank. He seems to be stopping everywhere, asking questions. Guess we'll find out when he gets here."

Morris' eyes widened. "I'm worried. I've got a feeling in my bones." All pro football teams have their "Nervous Nellies," and Frank Morris was New York's.

A complete pessimist, Morris was the type who would sight a ten-dollar bill lying in the gutter and moan that it was probably counterfeit before he ever picked it up. This character quirk off the field, however, didn't prevent him from being about the finest tight end in the league.

Wayne Draven approached, murmuring a few words to each man, receiving negative headshakes in response. Ronnie Baxter was reaching for his sweat pants when Draven neared.

"Hi, Ron. Morning, Frank. Either of you seen Harry Flood? The rest of the squad is here. He's overdue. I've called his house and nobody answers." Draven gnawed at his lower lip. He wasn't given to alarmism, yet it was obvious he chafed under a considerable burden of mental agitation.

"I haven't, Coach," said Ronnie. "Not since we left here yesterday. But then there wouldn't be any reason for me to. He lives in Stamford, doesn't he?"

"Right." Draven's answer was short, snapped out. "You, Frank? You have a place in Darien. You see each other during the week, I know."

Morris frowned. "Our wives talked on the phone earlier today, Coach. Mine stayed home because our car's being repainted. I took the train. Harry and his missus were driving in. She was supposed to keep their car and pick Harry up at the airport when we get back from Dallas. That's about all I can tell you—except any one of a dozen things might have made him late. Flat tire. Mechanical trouble. Jam-up on the turnpike, maybe."

"Yeah," grunted Draven, gazing with anxiety at his watch. "I suppose." He sounded far from convinced.

An undercurrent fanned out through the locker room like a swift-spreading breeze; it became a muted hum, a buzz, a murmur, a whisper of speculation. Draven's expressed concern over Flood's whereabouts had communicated itself to his players. They entered the training room to be taped, donned sneakers and sweat suits, sat around wondering as time passed, leaped to their feet almost as a man when the pay phone suddenly jangled.

Wayne Draven ran to it, lifted the receiver, and barked, "Clubhouse. Draven."

He listened for a few minutes. Little by little his face grew ashen. Twice he shook his head in shocked disbelief.

"Montefiore Hospital, you say, Tom? How long ago? Fifteen minutes? I see. They don't have any idea yet how bad, huh? His wife, too? Okay. Thanks, Tom. I'll be right over."

Draven hung up and wheeled to confront the Giants.

167

"Well, that really tears it. You can probably guess by now what the phone call was all about. It was from Lieutenant Tom Sallinger, an old buddy of mine on the New York police force."

A silent, apprehensive squad encircled him. Somehow, instinctively, they knew. The writers, sniffing a major story about to break, walked edgily around the outer perimeter of the group.

"Harry Flood, Coach?" Horse Collins asked in a low voice.

Draven nodded. "Yes. Incredibly bad news. Harry and his wife were on their way here, just as Frank told me. A couple of miles from the Stadium some nitwit ran a stop sign and clobbered them. Both cars are junk. The other driver's in serious condition. Harry's unconscious, and they've taken him to Montefiore Hospital. His wife's all right, they think, but they won't know for a while."

The quiet broke then in a series of sound waves that erupted into a confused babble. All the players attempted to talk at once, seeking further information, shooting questions at Draven for which the latter had no answers.

The coach held up a hand. "Now listen to me. There's no sense getting in an uproar until we learn all the facts. It may be no worse than a bump on the

168

head. I just don't know. But let's not jump to con-
clusions." Draven spoke to Bert Diehl. "Bert, you run
the drill. I'm leaving for the hospital. I'll be back as
soon as I find out anything definite."

Draven boiled out of the dressing room at a dead
run. The players wondered whether their last hopes
for the Eastern Conference title had vanished with
him. It was an appalling, outlandish stroke of misfor-
tune that had befallen them. First Chips Farrell lost
for the second half of the season, and now maybe
Harry Flood gone, too, virtually on the eve of their
crucial clash with the Cowboys!

Listlessly, as if all the will had drained from them,
the Giants went through their final tune-up paces
while awaiting their coach's return. Ronnie Baxter,
especially, was apprehensive. First and foremost, he
devoutly wished for Harry's safety, hence his avail-
ability for the key game against Dallas. The team,
which had struggled so hard during fourteen weeks
and now found their season compressed into a single
hour, deserved the experience represented by Flood at
the helm in the Cotton Bowl. Secondly, despite his
natural exuberance, Ronnie admitted to himself he
might be more than slightly fearful. As much as he had
desired to play and grumbled about riding the bench
and manning the intercom phones, there were easier

ways he could think of to be thrown into the starting quarterback's spot than in a game for the championship. With the stakes as high as they were, the normally white-hot temperature of the roaring inferno that was professional football would be redoubled.

An hour and a half resembling a century elapsed before Wayne Draven reappeared, making his way slowly up the concrete ramp that led from locker room to playing field at Yankee Stadium. One glance at his drawn countenance was sufficient. The news he bore was grim. He wasted no time imparting it to the squad.

"I'll lay it on the line to you," he told them. "Doctor Lotts says Harry's got a concussion. There's also a couple of broken ribs, plus a sprained right wrist. Mrs. Flood was shaken up and bruised some. Thank God it was no worse. But the driver's side absorbed most of the impact. They both wore seat belts, or they might have been killed.

"Doc says Harry'll be in the hospital awhile, until they run all the tests, check for double vision, things like that. Obviously he won't be on the field Sunday. I asked about the chances of having Harry back for the championship game with the West if we win, and Doc told me the chances were about fifty-fifty, but personally he was inclined to doubt it.

"However, we'll cross that bridge when we come to it. For now, Ronnie Baxter is the starting quarterback.

"One more word. Although I have the utmost confidence in Ron Baxter and his ability, there'll be a thousand pounds of pressure to the square inch on him. He's bound to make a mistake or two somewhere along the line. The rest of you people will just have to play a little harder to overcome them, that's all.

"Ronnie, come into the office with me. We have some talking to do."

As Ronnie trotted in the wake of his coach, the Giants numbly regarded each other and played a silent guessing game. They had survived the injury to Chips Farrell, turned back the challenge of the Cleveland Browns, and fought their way into a title shot. Was it possible for them to overcome this latest staggering blow, to scale the heights one more time with a rookie quarterback running the show?

It could be done, they agreed; rookie Bob Waterfield had led the old Cleveland Rams to the world title over the Washington Redskins in 1945. But could the Giants repeat this kind of miracle? That was the big question.

14 | *"Starting at Quarterback..."*

WHEN IT WAS all over, Ronnie Baxter never had any really clear recollection of the forty-eight hours that went by between Harry Flood's automobile accident and the opening kickoff in the Cotton Bowl.

It was, to him, a period of almost constant motion, an intense whirlwind of activity that occupied every waking moment, even carried over into two nights of restless sleep.

Impressions raced through Ronnie's mind. A quick visit to Flood at Montefiore, hours after the veteran had regained consciousness. A flood of excited gabble from sportswriters, into whose laps had been dumped, without warning, the stuff that drama—and, of course, circulation-building copy—was made of. Radio tapes galore. Three sound-on-film interviews for TV, two done in the Yankee Stadium dressing room, one at the airport waiting lounge. A long-distance telephone call from his father and mother in Oklahoma, soon after the team's Dallas arrival.

And of course there was Wayne Draven. The Giant coach never strayed far from his junior quarterback's side. He continually did his level best to shield Ronnie from some of the attention being showered on him. It proved a valiant, though futile, effort. No one man could have prevailed against the tidal wave of humanity that beseiged Ronnie from all sides.

Looking back on it, Ronnie wished all the reporters of the various press media might have packed their typewriters and microphones and gone home in a body. He realized such was neither logical nor very sensible on his part. Still, although some of his innate shyness had worn off since the initial days at training camp, Ronnie Baxter retained enough of it to desire just a few minutes' peace, an opportunity to wander off and work out his problems, to compose his mind alone. Then, at length, he sighed and resigned himself. He realized the newshounds and sportscasters had their jobs to do, the same as he did. Ronnie answered a hundred different queries in a dozen similar forms and still managed to smile.

In the bus, en route from the Dallas airport to the

team's hotel, they passed the huge electric sign near the downtown area that proclaimed the city as HOME OF THE COWBOYS—WORLD'S FASTEST TEAM.

Wayne Draven, sitting beside Ronnie in the rear section, pointed to it. "Things have changed some here the past couple of years," he said. "The fans, especially. The boo-birds used to jeer Dave Monroe to a fare-thee-well every time the offensive unit ran to the sideline, even when he had a good day. One of the Dallas players, I forget which one, was quoted in *Time Magazine* a while back. How did he put it? 'When I joined the club, if there was a crowd waiting at the airport when we returned from a game, we figured they had ropes.' That'll give you a rough idea. Now they jam into the Cotton Bowl seventy-five thousand strong nearly each home Sunday. Yet in 1961 the front office sold less than two thousand season tickets. It's nothing less than a bonanza, this pro football, Ronnie, and it keeps getting bigger every year. Of course, it helps if you've got a winner, too. By the way, how are you feeling? Worried? Tensed up?"

Ronnie knew Draven well enough by that time to realize that all the innocuous small talk was leading up to something.

"Okay, under the circumstances, I guess," Ronnie

replied cautiously. Deep inside him he knew he was drawn tighter than the skin stretched across a drumhead. In addition he wasn't naïve enough to believe that Draven didn't recognize the symptoms.

"I've wanted an opportunity to slide a few words in edgewise with you ever since yesterday morning." Draven began slowly. "With all that's happened, it's been pretty difficult.

"We're on a hot spot together, you and I, Ronnie, and there's nothing to do except make the best of it. I don't need to tell you that if Harry Flood were available, he'd play most of the game tomorrow, if not all. I don't want you to construe that as any rap on you or your ability. I repeat, I've got a world of confidence in you. It's just that in this league there's simply no substitute for experience. And that you don't have—yet."

Ronnie uncomfortably pressed sticky, clammy palms against each other. "Nobody knows it better than I, Coach," he said. "The more I think I'm learning, the more new angles I run into when I do play. There never seems to be an end to them."

"You're right, Ron. And once you've jammed the mechanics into your head, then you start picking up the nuances, the finer points. Take quarterbacks that've been around seven, eight, ten seasons, like Crimmins

175

at Green Bay, or Cleveland's Regan. They'll call a pass play, say, which sends a receiver downfield on a deep fly pattern. Assume the pass is missed or overthrown. On the very next play, one of those men I mentioned is liable to come right back with the same call, only sending a fresh man down in the same zone. Why? Because he figures the particular defender who covered the previous time has had a long run and may be just a shade slower on the second go-around. Would you have thought of that in the heat of battle?"

"No, I sure wouldn't," admitted Ronnie.

"Exactly. And who thinks you should after less than a full season in the National Football League? That's the point I'm making. You're good technically. You execute and fake well. You throw an accurate pass. You have all the tools. The main skill you lack at this stage is the knack of grasping the significance of the total picture at a given strategic moment, reading defenses, calling audibles at the line. No rookie can, with any great degree of success.

"Which leads me to what I started out to tell you. I'll shuttle the plays in to you tomorrow. We'll stick to the game plan as tightly as possible. Try to get ahead and force Dallas to catch up, using the running plays we talked over, throwing just enough to keep them honest, at the beginning, anyhow. Once again,

I don't want you to feel, Ronnie, that I'm trying to run the show at your expense. What I *am* attempting to do is take a bit of the pressure off you."

Ronnie nodded. He understood. As a matter of fact, he felt a trifle relieved. With Wayne Draven thus directing traffic from the bench, Ronnie would be much freer to concentrate on fundamentals.

"It's fine with me, Coach," Ronnie said, meaning it. "I just hope I don't let you down."

"Forget it," Draven replied gruffly. "You'll do all right."

Once in the hotel, time passed in slow, grudging units. Day finally yielded to night, and then it was day again. Ronnie found it difficult to distinguish between them as his own personal moment of truth in the NFL approached.

At last, arrival at the Cotton Bowl. Removal of street clothes. Taping of ankles. Sweatbands on wrists, because even close to Christmas the strong Texas sun had sent temperatures soaring to unseasonable levels. Donning the uniform. Out on the floor of the Cotton Bowl, already half full. Calisthenics, warm-up exercises designed to loosen muscles and sinews for the all-out effort nearly at hand. Back to the locker room for last-minute instructions, conferences with Draven, minor changes resulting from up-to-date information supplied by the assistant coaches.

Later, on the sideline once more, loosening up. Standing at rapt attention for the playing of the National Anthem under the warm sunshine. Introduction of players. Roar on roar of approval for the Cowboys from the 75,000 or more rabid fans jamming the stadium as their offensive unit came on one by one.

Then the Giants' turn. Finally, after an eon, the public-address system booming out, "Starting at quarterback for New York, number nineteen, six-feet two, one hundred and ninety-five pounds, from Tulsa University, Ron Baxter!" A small, ragged cheer floating up. Ronnie, seeing the whole panorama only as a blur of green, white, blue, gray, and silver, racing out onto the middle of the field through the lanes formed by members of the Dallas marching group, the Apache Belles. On the 50, joining Collins, Pyle, Pell, Morris, Strawbridge, Matson, McGuire, Bellson, Payson, and Arnie Jennings. Shaking hands all around. Tossing words of encouragement to each other, echoed by the kicking unit as they came on the field.

The Cowboys had won the coin flip and elected to receive. Twenty-two players arranged themselves in standard formations at either end of the turf. Bobo

Zarilla raised his right arm. The striped-shirted referee blew his whistle, while the noise from the stands built to an earsplitting crescendo. Zarilla ran forward, put his toe into the ball, and the game for the Eastern Conference crown was under way.

Dallas' Rick Cables was back deep along with Jim Tabors. Zarilla's boot carried short to the 10. Cables fielded it there, returned to the 15, was hit, fumbled forward, and recovered on the Dallas 18.

On the very first play, the Giants' defense went into an "odd-man-line" set, with linebackers darting in and out of the gaps, one man nose-to-nose with the offensive center, to throw the Dallas blocking assignments out of kilter as much as possible right at the outset. Noting this, quarterback Dave Monroe checked off at the line, resetting his backfield and sending his fullback, Paul Parsons, inside tackle. Ron Lewis, the Giants' middle linebacker, threw him for a loss. Monroe next tried a draw to Parsons, but the Giants shot Lyndon Bentley in on a safety blitz. Bentley nailed Parsons for a 3-yard loss, bringing up third and 14. When Monroe sought to put the ball in the air, all his receivers were covered, so he simply ducked under an enemy arm and ran for 9. Darrell Forrester, Dallas' fine punter and field goal specialist, booted a high spiral that rolled dead on the New York 38.

"All right, Ronnie, go get 'em," Wayne Draven barked. "Call the plays we drilled on in sequence for the first series. After that we'll see how we're set up and what their defense does."

There was a buzzing, ringing sound inside Ronnie's helmet, and sweat had already begun to drip from beneath it when he placed his opened hands under Al McGuire's rump and chanted the signals. Ronnie thought he had been beset by butterflies prior to the first preseason game with the Steelers at Ithaca, and so he had. Nevertheless, he conceded that that occasion's attack of jitters was small potatoes by comparison.

Somehow he managed to grasp the exchange cleanly, slap the ball into Willie Collins' belly, and step back out of the way. The "Horse" slanted over left tackle, picking up 4 to the New York 42. Still moving in a comparative daze, Ronnie watched Ed Pell jog in motion to the left, with the weak-side linebacker moving out laterally to cover him. Ronnie dropped straight back into the pocket, received good blocking, and threw a down-and-out toward his flanker, George Pyle. It wasn't a particularly accurate pass, but the nimble, sure-handed Pyle assured a completion, curling back and grabbing the low, underthrown ball off the grass on the Dallas 41.

In the huddle, Ronnie banged him on the shoulder pads. "You made me look like a champ on that one, George," the quarterback said. "Nice catch."

"Just keep throwing, Ron. No sweat," Pyle replied.

Switching slightly from his original game plan, which called for establishment of the ground attack, Draven was apparently of the same mind. With Pell again in motion, Ronnie hit him on a quick swing that carried for a 5-yard gain to the Dallas 36 before Art Jurgens, the Cowboys' veteran middle linebacker, bore Pell to earth. Then, with second and 5, Collins was held to no gain on a power-lead sweep left. Booker T. Bellson, one of the Giants' pulling guards, missed his block and allowed Dallas' right linebacker to crash through for the tackle. Ronnie next threw deep and incomplete to Ed Pell, running a post pattern, on the goal line. The Cowboys' secondary coverage had been excellent, Ronnie noted; he had thrown the ball away, more than anything else, to avoid an interception.

Bobo Zarilla and the kicking unit came on, but the field goal try from 43 yards out swooped low and to the right. On the touchback, Dallas regained possession on their 20.

The first eight minutes of the opening period settled down to a battle of toes. Both teams took turns punting, waiting for an initial break. Les Tremont, the

Giant kicker, got off boots of 46 and 51 yards, keeping Dallas pinned fairly deep in its own territory. Darrell Forrester was only slightly less effective for Dallas. Bobo Zarilla missed another field goal attempt, at extreme long range, Ronnie holding on the Dallas 47.

It was soon obvious to commentators and press-box observers that Remmie Braun's odd-man-line and shifting defenses were bothering Dave Monroe. The Dallas quarterback experimented with various methods of combating them, none very successful. They included a quick count play, one that developed on "first sound," and repeated use of the power-I formation to utilize an extra blocker.

Late in the first quarter, Jim Tabors returned a Les Tremont punt 17 yards to the Dallas 49. Parsons gained two on a quick opener. Trying to throw on second and long, Monroe found all his receivers blanketed, tucked the ball under his arm, and tight-roped down the far sideline for 8 yards and an apparent first down. However, a penalty marker had been thrown. The Cowboys were penalized back to their 46; illegal procedure was the call.

Dallas came out in a slot left, with second and 13. Intending to go deep to his flanker, who had run a stop-and-go, Monroe found himself rushed hard by the Giants' outside linebackers, Lou Slabodnick and

Bull Durham. He was forced to flip the ball, on a safety-valve pass, out to his fullback, Parsons. The latter plowed for 7 yards to the New York 47 as the scoreless first period drew to a close.

When the two teams changed ends of the field, the Dallas attack resumed uninterruptedly. Spreading the defense wider with a double-slot set, Monroe faked a pass, then carried on the quarterback draw 11 yards to the Giant 36.

On the sideline, agitatedly watching the chain gang move the sticks to conform with the Dallas first down, Wayne Draven had already nearly worn a trench with his nervous pacing. He alternately listened on the phones, shouted instructions, and encouraged his embattled defensive unit.

Monroe tossed a flare pass which fell incomplete to the flanker, Mark Alson, as New York's defensive right end, Al Waskoff, fired through to harass Monroe and cause him to get rid of the ball in a hurry.

Next a key play cropped up that kept Dallas' sustained drive alive. From his split end position, the familiar and mercurial Bill Barton, who had served as a decoy in the early going, raced deep into the far left corner. He pulled double coverage, as he had all afternoon, from the weak-side linebacker and free safety. With the flow of the action thus going left,

Monroe had his tight end, Bernie Green, take the ball on an end around to the opposite flank. It worked like a charm. The Giants' other safety, Lyndon Bentley, finally shoulder-blocked Green out-of-bounds on the New York 24. Dallas had racked up a second consecutive first down.

"Remmie, I warned them about the end around!" Draven fumed on the phones to his chief defensive expert. "They really got themselves suckered on that one."

"I know, Coach," said Braun wryly. "They made up their minds where the play was going before it started. Barton's hurting us more as a threat than if they were actually throwing to him."

A quick look-in to flanker Mark Alson moved the ball 5 yards closer, to the Giants' 19. From there Monroe handed off to Paul Parsons, who benefited from a great initial block by the Cowboys' left tackle, Jess Merriwether. Parsons burst through the hole, broke two tackles beyond the line, squirmed away from Hal Honegger, and stumbled into the end zone. Darrell Forrester split the uprights. Early in the second period, Dallas had hung the go-ahead tally on the scoreboard and led 7 to 0.

Following the kickoff the Dallas defense forced a punt. However, New York took the football right back when Ron Lewis, blitzing from his middle linebacker post, dumped Monroe and separated him from the pigskin. Jim Karnarveron recovered, and the Giants were in business on the Cowboys' 40.

"Way to go, Buddha, way to go!" Draven chortled when the defensive unit trotted toward the bench.

Ronnie gummed up a hand-off to Collins; the fullback was stopped for no gain. Ed Pell swept right end, making 6 yards, and almost broke away before the Cowboys' right cornerback dropped him. Ronnie's pass blocking fizzled on the third-down play, and his hasty safety-valve peg to Collins fell behind the fullback.

It was fourth and 4 from the Dallas 34. Draven sent Bobo Zarilla in. The Giants' kicker had already blown two long-distance attempts with the wind at his back. Now he faced a third effort against it, almost 42 yards away. Ronnie placed the snap down squarely and efficiently. Zarilla moved into it. Ronnie heard the solid *thunk* that told his practiced ear the boot was on target. It was high enough . . . far enough . . . and good! Field judge and back judge threw arms skyward. The Dallas lead was sliced to 7–3.

On the ensuing kickoff Cables and Tabors played Alphonse and Gaston with the ball, each assuming the other would handle it, with the result that neither did. Cables finally decided not to bring it out of the end zone.

Monroe pitched out to Max Waters, his running back, good for 7 yards to the 27 behind a crunching block thrown by Jess Merriwether which erased two New York defenders. Paul Nestor, the Giants' right tackle, apparently recovered a Dallas fumble right after that, but the whistle had blown the play dead at the line.

Draven was livid. He danced up and down the sideline, intensely angry, hurling imprecations at the officials.

"Come on, you guys, get in the ball game, will you?" he pleaded. "Lay off that quick whistle! You just cost us a recovery!"

When the Giants took over at their 39 moments later on a Darrell Forrester punt, Ronnie Baxter wasted no time. Acting on information brought back to the huddle by Arnie Jennings that the Dallas cornerbacks and one safety were closing in rapidly on apparent running sequences (and additionally finding the play that he himself would have called sent in from the bench), Ronnie set the wheels in motion. First he opened the distance between his backs. Then he handed off to Willie Collins, who started sweeping right. The Giants' fullback, in turn, reversed to Ed

Pell coming the other way. Nearing the line of scrimmage, Pell suddenly stopped in his tracks, cocked his arm, and lofted a high floater to the split end, Arnie Jennings. Even though covered closely man-for-man by the weak-side corner defender, Jennings hauled it in on the Dallas 27 to complete a 34-yard razzler-dazzler!

From there, sandwiching running plays around a completed pass to Jennings on a square-out pattern, Ronnie guided his team to another first down on the Dallas 14. He sent Collins up the middle behind a key block by offensive center Al McGuire all the way to the 2. Belted high and low simultaneously, Collins coughed up the football. The Cowboys' middle linebacker, Art Jurgens, scooped it up and ran down the near sideline for 31 yards to the 33. The Cotton Bowl fans went out of their collective mind as the Giant offensive unit trudged unhappily off the field.

Collins was beside himself, smacking one fist into his other palm, muttering over and over, "Touchdown! A sure touchdown, and I blew it!"

Ronnie punched him lightly on the forearm. "Forget it, Horse," he said, knowing the depths of misery the fullback felt, how he himself curdled a little inside each time he fouled up a hand-off or overthrew a receiver in the clear. "We'll get it back. Don't worry."

Ronnie was right. Monroe caught the Giants guessing in a first-down red dog, with resultant single coverage on Barton, and hit the split end with a bullet on the New York 44. The officials, though, had detected holding on the part of Dallas. A 15-yard penalty nullified the gain and set the Cowboys back to the 18, where it became first and 25. Paul Parsons gained a scant yard on a trap. Then Monroe connected with a screen pass to running back Max Waters. Convoyed by blockers, Waters picked up 20 yards to the Dallas 39, but again a yellow penalty marker lay on the field. This time the referee placed both hands on his cap, indicating an ineligible receiver had somehow found his way downfield. The Cowboys walked slowly back to their huddle. The half-the-distance penalty put the ball on the 9, second and 34.

Gunner Swenson, the Giants' left cornerback, who had made the tackle on the preceding play, was shaken up and had to be helped off the field. Half groggy, but still wanting to stay in, Swenson argued with Yogi Di Orio and Wayne Draven, then waved away his replacement, Weldon Smythe. He was finally persuaded, with difficulty, to sit down on the bench and sniff some oxygen. Ronnie smiled. It was so typical, he thought. Pride. Toughness, mixed with just a little stubbornness. They all had it, up here in the National

Football League, in great quantities.

From his 9, Dave Monroe set up to throw. The Giants again poured everybody in on the blitz. The Dallas quarterback tried evasive tactics, scrambling around near the goal line, actually once crossing over into the end zone. The apprehension of the crowd was audible as Monroe flirted with a safety. He barely got out, only to be buried on the ½-yard line. Upcoming was third and 42.

A third-down quarterback sneak picked up less than a yard. The Cowboys were forced to punt from deep in their own territory.

Darrell Forrester, standing a foot from the end line, readied himself to punt out. Shorn of his customary 15-yard protective cushion, his hurried kick had barely left his foot when the Giants' defensive right end, Al Waskoff, barreled through and smothered the kick. Ron Lewis fell on it in the end zone. Touchdown, New York! When Bobo Zarilla added the conversion, the Giants had taken the lead at 10–7, with just over two minutes remaining in the half.

Monroe immediately initiated his two-minute drill. Starting from the Dallas 37, he passed complete to the tight end, Bernie Green, for 15 yards to the New York 48. Paul Parsons chewed up 11, and the Cowboys had a first down on the 37. The last two plays had been run without a huddle. Since the clock was moving, Monroe killed it by calling time-out.

When play was resumed, Monroe felt the weight of the Giants' pass rush. Hal Honegger, from weak safety, and Ron Lewis, the middle linebacker, were both in on Monroe like a shot, forcing him to unload the ball rather than eat it.

Sensing another red dog coming, Monroe called an audible at the line to turn the maneuver to his advantage. He whipped the ball to the fullback in the vacant zone around the middle; Parsons shrugged off a tackler, evaded another, and bulled his way into the end zone.

The jubilation of the Dallas fans, however, was short-lived. The officials had called offensive pass interference on Parsons! They had caught him pushing Lyndon Bentley, the Giant free safety, who had switched to covering Parsons when Ron Lewis went in on the blitz. The ball came back to the Dallas 48. Giant supporters breathed more easily, since the Cowboys were, for the moment at least, out of field goal range.

With nineteen seconds showing on the clock and Dallas again at the New York 35, Ron Lewis hit Monroe hard as the quarterback threw incomplete to Alson, the flanker, on a quick look-in. Monroe limped off the field, assisted by the trainer and team physician.

Concern lined their faces. Were Monroe unable to play the second half, the Dallas attack would be badly hampered.

Darrell Forrester's fourth-down, 42-yard field goal attempt, with a following breeze that had reached some ten miles per hour, drifted wide to the right. The Giants ran for their dressing room at intermission owning a 10–7 lead.

Draven made a point of speaking to Ronnie Baxter alone, off to one side, just before the teams took the field for the start of the final thirty minutes.

"You're doing fine, Ronnie," the coach said. "Looks like the knots are untied now."

Ronnie nodded. "More or less. If anybody had ever told me I'd be this collected playing in a title game my first season, I'd have thought he was some kind of a nut. Don't ask me about that opening series, though, Coach. I won't remember any of it until I see the films."

"It appears the hollering I did back in July and August is paying off, even if you did dislike me for it. Just keep on the way you're going. We may get a break in the second half if Monroe can't come back. It'll mean either of the two rookies running the club, with Collison calling the plays from the bench. And if I had to bet on which coach will get the better execution out of his quarterback, I'd take myself, because you're in there pitching."

Ronnie was walking on cloud nine as he loosened up on the sideline, while Dallas prepared to kick off to the Giants. It was the most expansive praise he had yet received from Wayne Draven, the old master psychologist when he had to be. Ronnie couldn't be sure if Draven were putting him on or not; in any case, the youngster was shrewd enough to realize he ought not to claim much personal credit for field generalship, what with Draven shuttling each offensive decision in to him via messenger.

Nonetheless, even with these tempering considerations, Ronnie felt elation of a sort he had never experienced before creeping over him. While one game, or a full season for that matter, did not make a pro quarterback, Ronnie Baxter had begun to achieve a sense of belonging, of finding himself, of at long last beginning to fit into the proper Giant niche.

After Forrester's kickoff, Ronnie soon had to wrestle with a third and 11 from the Giants' 22. Collins, plus the two tackles, Don Payson and Jack Strawbridge, did an excellent job of holding off the determined Dallas blitzers for an instant, but eventually they swarmed in on Ronnie. Harassed, hemmed in, he heaved the ball wildly in the general direction of his primary receiver, Frank Morris. The Dallas strong safety plucked it out of the air on the Giants' 42 and returned, with a twisting, tackle-busting run, all the way to the 19.

Annoyed at himself, Ronnie bounced his helmet on the ground when he came back to the bench. Wayne Draven observed the petulant act.

"That isn't going to do much good," the latter observed mildly, masking the seething turmoil eating him up inside. "As I mentioned in the Steeler game at Ithaca before the season started, there's a time to release the ball and a time to hang on to it."

Ronnie inclined his head, staring at the ground. "I know, Coach. My fault. I fired into a crowd. I should have simply thrown it away, seeing Frank was covered." Wretchedly Ronnie figured he had reabsorbed a valuable, if expensive, lesson. Draven had warned all the younger players at Fairfield that there existed a far greater emphasis on pass defense in the NFL than in college, that any ball hung up high would find four defenders waiting for it to descend. In addition it had now become obvious to Ronnie that one couldn't afford to allow a coach's words of commendation to go to one's head either.

Dave Monroe failed to appear with the Dallas offensive unit. Word circulated around the Giant bench that he had suffered a twisted knee. Blackie

Collison, the Cowboys' able young mentor, shuttled his rookie quarterbacks on each play, a ploy Draven hadn't foreseen. One was Pete Hildebrand, like Ronnie a Tulsa graduate of a year earlier. The other was Carl Farber, who had played at California.

Dallas broke the huddle and came out in a slot left. Andy Robertson, from his defensive end post, slammed Parsons to the ground after the fullback picked up 2 yards to the Giant 17. A halfback draw to Max Waters was stacked up for no gain. Farber, on a right roll-out, passed incomplete to his tight end on the New York 8. The Cowboys had run out of downs, and the kicking unit made its appearance. Darrell Forrester toed a 24-yard field goal that tied the score at 10–10.

With five minutes left in the third period Dallas was treated to a big break, one the ballplayers are wont to call a "piece of cake." The Giant defense held, bringing up a punt situation. Paul Nestor very nearly effected a block, but a flag was dropped when he was detected roughing Forrester. It was a clear infraction of Rule 10, Section 2, Article 2. The field judge stood right on top of the play, noting that Nestor had rolled into Forrester without touching the ball. Finally no one in the Cotton Bowl knew any better than Nestor that he had indeed fouled the kicker, albeit unintentionally.

Thus given a new lease on life, plus the ball on their own 23, the Cowboys covered the distance in seven plays. Hildebrand faked a wide pitch to Parsons, then sent Max Waters, the running back, wriggling for a tough 5 with a quick inside hand-off. Carl Farber threw to the tight end, Bernie Green, on a sideliner that resulted in a first down at the Dallas 38.

The "World's Fastest Human," Bill Barton, the Cowboys' split end, who had been used mostly as a decoy to that point, ran a neat curl pattern. Hildebrand hit him squarely on the money at the New York 44, a gain of 18 yards and another first down.

Parsons, with a fine cutback maneuver and change of stride, went over left tackle to the 35 before Ron Lewis stopped him. Hildebrand's pitchout to Waters for no gain brought up a third and 1 at the 35. Farber, as Collison suspected he would, stared at a Giant line jammed up in the middle, geared in a virtual goal-line defense to smother the inevitable running play. It is axiomatic in a setup such as that that the smart coach or quarterback calls whatever has been going well, the play that gets to the line of scrimmage in the greatest hurry. The fullback, Parsons, following a long count, rammed into the pack, broke clear amid the depleted secondary, and with tremendous second effort rambled 12 vital yards down to the 23.

From there Farber connected with Barton again on a short flare pattern. The Dallas speedster, aided by a great block on Ron Lewis from his tight end, Bernie Green, who seemed to be everywhere, took it in for the TD. Forrester's conversion thrust Dallas into the lead again, 17 to 10.

Very little time remained in the third period. The Giants retaliated. From the New York 48, Ronnie handed off to Ed Pell. The halfback found no running room in the center of the line where his hole was supposed to be. Instead he reversed direction, cut to the outside, turned the corner, and sped all the way to the Dallas 11 on a 41-yard jaunt. He was caught from behind by the enemy safety, who had the outside angle on the ball carrier.

Alertly noting the safety man's long scamper to overtake Pell, Draven ordered Ronnie to come right back with a pass to Pell's understudy, Jack Michaels, who would in the normal course of events be covered in the deep zone by the same defender.

It worked to perfection. Michaels beat his man by a step. Ronnie lobbed a high floater over the safety's head into the hands of the Giants' reserve halfback in the extreme left corner of the end zone. Bobo Zarilla calmly split the uprights with the tying point, then kicked off to Dallas. Jim Tabors ran it back to the Cowboys' 33 from the 8 as the third quarter ended.

The two teams stood deadlocked at 17–17. The labors of an entire season for the two conference contenders would be wrapped up in a final, frenzied fifteen minutes of football!

15 | *The Final Gun*

WHILE DRAVEN nearly went into apoplexy, first Hildebrand, then Farber were seemingly trapped behind the line by Giant defenders. Somehow, though, they managed to scoot free and run for sizable gains, 8 yards at a clip, moving the ball up to the Dallas 49. After that the New York blitzers, alternating with relentless pressure from the front four, reached both young quarterbacks. But on third and 19, Farber found his tight end at the last moment with a sideline pass, and Dallas had a first down on the New York 39. The Giant defense held, and the Cowboys only managed four yards on the next three plays. On fourth and five from the New York 35, the Dallas field goal team came in. Despite a determined rush from Gunner Swenson and Lou Slabodnick, Forrester got the kick off. It barely cleared the crossbar, but it was long enough to send Dallas into a 20–17 fourth-quarter lead.

The kickoff went out of the end zone, and the New Yorkers started from their own 20. The Giants picked up 5 yards on their first two downs, but when flanker George Pyle dropped Ronnie Baxter's third-down sideline pass, they had to give up the football. Les Tremont booted dead on the Dallas 26.

Hildebrand handed off to fullback Paul Parsons, who spun away from a Ron Lewis tackle and went for 7 yards. Farber pitched out wide to Max Waters, and the Dallas runner saw daylight. Gaining the outside behind a devastating block from his right tackle that chopped down Andy Robertson on the Giants' left flank, Waters ballet-danced his way down the far stripe for 67 yards and the third Dallas 6-pointer. An indescribable din filled the Cotton Bowl for the second time that quarter when the Cowboys thus took a commanding 27–17 edge with just over ten minutes left.

"Okay, Ron, work on that safety man again," Draven advised on the sideline. "You beat him the last time with Michaels. He may be hearing the thunder of hooves by now. I want to see if Collison orders double coverage. If he does, that should leave somebody else open."

Following instructions to the letter, Ronnie drilled

a perfect pass to Pell up around the New York 40. Faking one defender out of his path, Pell flew for 32 yards to the Dallas 28. Ronnie threw incomplete to Pyle in the end zone, then came back with a pitch to Arnie Jennings, the split end. Jennings, who had run a slant-and-go pattern, brought the ball to a first down on the Dallas 10½. Continuing the aerial probing, Ron missed Pell racing for the posts. The Giants were in motion illegally on the play, but the Cowboys' defensive captain, after having been informed of the options by the referee, declined the penalty.

"They had two people on me that time, Ron," Pell reported in the huddle. "Just as the coach guessed. A linebacker picked me up short, then the safety double-covered me deep."

Bill Lattington, who had been switched earlier in the season from defensive swing tackle and "Kamikaze Squad" member to strictly offensive lineman, came shuttling in with a play.

"Coach says go to Frank Morris with the down-and-in. The other safety's handling him man-for-man. Make sure you throw it high. Frank's got four or five inches on Johnson."

Ronnie called the cadence, grabbed the ball at the first "Hut!" and drifted back quickly. With two men hovering about him, Pell had cleared the zone to the right. Ronnie arched the ball into the opposite corner, at the goal line. Frank Morris leaped like a basketball player going up for a rebound, beating his defender's short, late jump, and glued his fingertips on the leather. They rolled over in the end zone together. Ronnie Baxter held, Bobo Zarilla swung his leg, and an ecstatic end zone fan had a souvenir. With seven minutes and forty-seven seconds left, New York trailed by a field goal, 27–24.

Ronnie sat down on the bench reveling in the glow of real accomplishment. He had thrown two scoring passes, both well executed, against the most rock-ribbed defense in the Eastern Conference. He felt good, even more so when Draven looked in his direction and spared a second for an approving nod before turning his attention back toward the field.

Zarilla's kickoff sailed end-over-end deep to the Dallas 1. Rick Cables brought it out to the 27. Setting up a slot-right formation, Hildebrand lived dangerously by throwing a pass into the flat, intended for Bill Barton. It fell incomplete, almost intercepted. Farber, instructed by Collison to anticipate a Giant red dog, waited until the last split second, just before being swarmed under, to flip a screen out to Mark Alson. The Dallas flanker was finally tackled at the Cowboys' 40-yard line. Hildebrand pitched out to

Max Waters, starting a left sweep. Aided by the pulling right guard's key block on Lou Slabodnick, the Giants' weak-side linebacker, Waters turned the corner and sped 25 yards to the New York 35. Sensing victory, the partisan Dallas crowd unleashed an incredible flood of noise. Carl Farber, in for the next play, had to raise his arms in an appeal for quiet so the team could hear the signals.

The former California All-American, noted for his shifty running in college as much as his pinpoint passing, rolled right. The flow of the action moved with him. He suddenly halted, pivoted, and flung a deep diagonal pass to the left. Bill Barton, running a simple sprint-out maneuver, had shaken himself loose from cornerback Bill Johnson for a moment. Barton made a circus catch on the New York 6. Although Johnson, with Honegger's help, dropped him in his tracks, it was first and goal, Dallas!

Hildebrand entered the scene, under Blackie Collison's rotating-quarterback plan, and rammed the ball into Paul Parson's belly. The big fullback slashed into a gaping hole created over left tackle on a trap of Paul Nestor, then found clear sailing when Bernie Green, Dallas' tight end, wiped Ron Lewis out with an effective block. Parsons cantered into pay dirt untouched as 75,000 people went wild. After Darrell Forrester added the conversion, the Cowboys led the Giants, 34–24, with the clock showing three minutes and fifty-eight seconds to go!

"Start your two-minute drill early," Draven told Ron, his face bleak, sending the rookie quarterback from the bench with the offensive unit. "We need to score twice now. Conserve as much time as you can. No matter where a play originates, try to have the man with the ball wriggle out-of-bounds. Throw the sideline passes. Don't huddle. Call the plays in sequence, the way we practiced them. Above all, don't use any time-outs yet. If we take it in, we'll have to use an onside kick and regain possession right away. We're in a tough spot, but there's still enough time left. Okay. Our ball on the thirty-four. In you go."

On the first play, the Ronnie Baxter–Wayne Draven combination called for a screen pass to Ed Pell on the right. Defenders were sucked in and soon regretted their rash eagerness to blitz Ronnie out of his cleats. With the football in his hands, the Giants' running back found himself with four teammates waiting to escort him down the near sideline. Methodically, one by one, they mopped up would-be tacklers, the safety man last. Pell ran on into the end zone to complete a 68-yard scoring burst, flinging the football up into the stands in a spasm of pure joy. When Bobo Zarilla

brought them back within three points, at 34–31, the electric clock showed three minutes and nineteen seconds remaining, and the Giants were back in the thick of things!

Bobo Zarilla ran over to the New York bench. "You still want me to try the onside kick, Coach?" he inquired. "We scored so fast I thought maybe you wanted to change the strategy."

Draven hesitated. It was a tough decision to make. If he ordered Zarilla to kick the ball deep in the normal manner, Dallas might well make a first down and run out the clock. Even if they didn't, they would squander so much time on ground plays, plus taking the full thirty seconds to set each in motion, that to all intents and purposes the inexorably ticking seconds would kill the Giants.

On the other hand, granting a recovery of the onside boot, the Giants would be in good field position, and in addition they would have the ball. Draven was a gambler when necessary, and this was definitely the spot for it. It was all or nothing. Go for broke. During the span of half a heartbeat, Wayne Draven reflected how nice it might be to enjoy the luxury of having the lead in a situation like this, as Blackie Collison did. Thus the mental coaching wheels ground, and in five short seconds the answer came.

"Kick it short, Bobo," said Draven. "Make sure those front people are alert. If Dallas does recover, try to jar the ball loose on the tackle."

Zarilla nodded. He teed up the ball, the whistle blew, and Zarilla nudged the ball off the side of his foot, trying to judge the angle and force properly so it would go ten yards and still stay in bounds.

The kick did both, bouncing around crazily on the Dallas 48 or 49. A constant babble of sound filled the Cotton Bowl. A Dallas man had his hands on the leather, then a Giant, and finally the Cowboys came up with it on their 45. Two minutes and fifty-nine seconds remained.

Collison's club took all the time it was legally entitled to. Hildebrand ran three consecutive quarterback sneaks into the massed muscle of the line, gaining a total of four yards. The Dallas coach had so instructed him with two basic purposes in mind—to utilize the clock, and also to minimize the possibility of a fumble that was always present on even the simplest hand-off. When Darrell Forrester hoisted a towering punt, rolling the ball out-of-bounds on the Giant 8, there were fifty-seven seconds left and 92 yards to travel.

Omitting a huddle, breaking on first sound, Ronnie threw a short pass complete to Arnie Jennings on a down-and-out maneuver at the 15. The split end immediately stepped across the sideline to stop the clock, which showed fifty-two seconds.

The Cowboys, of course, were sitting pretty. All they had to do was to keep New York out of field goal range. They had gone into their 3-4-4 "prevent" defense, conceding Ronnie the short stuff—6, 7, 8 yards on hooks, flares, square-outs—realizing that the rookie's field of endeavor was limited due to poor field position and the time element.

The Giants crossed their hands in the T signal for a time-out after the next play, since Collins slipped and was unable to quite get off the field after having grabbed a swing pass from Ronnie. It gained 6 and a Giant first down at their 21, but the clock told its sad story—thirty-one seconds. Ronnie used the second New York time-out of the half and ran to the bench.

"You'll have to throw the long bomb, Ron. No getting around it, risk of interception from the umbrella or not. We can't use that many short pass plays to take us into field goal range. Go to Jennings on the fly. It's your best bet now."

Ronnie nodded and swallowed. The bitter taste of defeat burned in his mouth. All of a sudden the youngster felt terribly fatigued and old beyond his years.

He tried his best, but it simply was not to be. With

an extra defender back deep and the split end well blanketed, Ronnie rolled out of the pocket, searching for his secondary target, George Pyle. The strong-side cornerback went deep with Pyle, matching him stride for stride. Then the defender seemed to stumble momentarily, and Ronnie saw a chance. Putting all the strength he possessed into the last-gasp effort, he whipped the football in a high spiral toward the streaking flanker.

As the Dallas fans let out a startled roar, it seemed as if Ronnie had pulled the Giant chestnuts from the fire. But at the last possible second, with a Conference championship riding on his reflexes, the free safety switched off Ed Pell, darted over, and grabbed the ball out of Pyle's hands. Pyle downed him instantly, but without question it was all done for New York.

Dallas ran one play into the line, following the Giants' calling of their third and last time-out. Despairingly, Ronnie, on the bench, saw the line judge raise his gun. The countdown chant from the stands echoed, as from a great distance, to his ears: *"Four ... three ... two ... one ... zero!"* Ronnie saw the tiny puff of smoke from the pistol, but couldn't hear its report because the Cotton Bowl erupted into a veritable torrent of cheers, shrieks, yells, and screams. People poured onto the field, hoisted Dallas players and their coach,

Blackie Collison, atop willing shoulders, and prepared to bear them in victorious delirium to the dressing room.

It took Ronnie a few seconds for the numbing realization to sink in fully. The game was finished, and so were Giant hopes. Dallas had won the wild and woolly contest 34—31, and thereby had also won the right to meet the Packers in Green Bay for the National Football League title!

Shoulders slumped, head down, reliving in his mind every peak and valley of the bruising football game just concluded, Ronnie Baxter walked slowly with his teammates to the visiting locker area. Once there, the postgame inquisition at the hands of writers and photographers began. Somewhat to his surprise, Ronnie found himself sharing equal billing with Wayne Draven. The two were snapped from various angles, alone and together, to the accompaniment of popping flashbulbs. Then the scribes closed in.

"Don't know whether you're aware of it or not," one of them said, poising his pencil, "but you were eighteen out of twenty-seven passing, with three touchdowns and two hundred and seventy-eight yards gained. Pretty good afternoon in your first starting assignment. How do you feel about it?"

"Okay, I guess," the weary Ronnie replied. "Naturally I'd feel a lot better if we'd won. And let's not forget they intercepted me twice. The last one was the ball game, too."

"Refreshing candor," somebody else remarked. "What are your winter plans, Ronnie?"

The sweat-streaked quarterback shrugged. "A little hunting with my father and my old college coach, Charley Tubbs. Afterward I'll help out with spring football practice at Tulsa. Maybe some basketball to keep my legs in shape. Outside of that, not very much."

"Draven was calling all the plays from the bench," said a third writer. "If you'd had a free hand to run the game as you saw fit, do you think you'd have done anything differently?"

"No comment," Ron snapped, shaking his head. "I wouldn't second-guess the coach even if I had any basis for doing it. We scored thirty-one points against the stingiest defense in the league, which speaks for itself."

Eventually the cross-examination ground to a halt. Ronnie was incredibly tired, he found. He dragged himself into the shower, soaped vigorously, allowed the hot, stinging spray to wash some of his empty, letdown emotions away with the lather. The figures the sportswriter had quoted to him were interesting, Ronnie thought. Even indicative he could hold his

211

own in a tough league. But what did they really mean when measured against the infinitely larger reality of the victory that had won it all for Dallas.

Wrapping a towel around his waist, Ronnie padded toward his locker. There, in the almost hushed quiet that invariably reigned in the losers' quarters, he discovered Wayne Draven waiting for him.

"Nice game, Ron," the coach said, mustering a faint smile. "You played like a pro." It was a high compliment indeed, coming as it did from Draven.

Ronnie reached for his shirt. "I just wish I could have done more—like throwing a touchdown pass in the last thirty seconds, instead of being intercepted."

"Well, you didn't and that's that. To use the oldest cliché in the books, you can't win 'em all. A man can do his utmost, sometimes rise to an occasion even beyond that, and lose anyway. There's always next season and the one after. I can afford to be fatalistic now, since this year's gone by the boards. You play each game as it arrives. Another Sunday's always in the offing. Eventually you run out of Sundays. When you do, start making plans for next season. It's as simple as that."

It suddenly dawned on Ronnie what Draven was hinting at. "But—the newspapers—all those rumors—that if we didn't win—"

212

"It isn't generally known yet, and won't be until the official announcement comes out in a week or two, so I expect you to keep your lip buttoned. Anyhow, the owners figured second place was good enough for a team that suffered all the key injuries we did, especially to quarterbacks. They're renewing my contract for five years."

Ronnie's face broke into a broad grin. "Glad to hear it, Coach. It'll be like old home week, come July in Fairfield. And I know I'll be a lot handier at relaying information on the phones than I was this past season."

"You crazy?" snorted Draven. "You've developed fast. You have as good a chance as anybody of winding up number one quarterback. Doctor Lotts swears Chips Farrell will be one hundred percent okay again, but with knees you never can tell. Harry Flood isn't getting any younger. I told you before, you have all the tools. Today just confirmed my opinion. When you learn to use them properly, to pick away at little holes in the defense until they become big ones, when you are able to call automatics at the line fifty percent of the time, you've got it made." Draven looked at his watch. "It's late. I'll see you in the bus."

The Giants' head coach hurried away. Ronnie knotted his tie, shrugged into his jacket, and picked up the leather kit containing his toilet articles. He joined

Bruiser Kinarski, Les Tremont, and Arnie Jennings. Together they left the locker room and wandered out into the warm Texas evening.

Ronnie pondered Draven's words, and some of the anguished discontent he had experienced earlier fell from him.

The loss to the Cowboys lay in the past. Dwelling on it wouldn't change the final score one iota. The future was what counted. It loomed bright and long, stretching toward horizons Ronnie couldn't yet begin to envision.

Ronnie Baxter, rookie. Ronnie Baxter, pro quarterback. He knew now that in the National Football League the two designations were light-years apart. There remained much to be done before he finally bridged the gulf between them.

However, Ronnie thought, a full season at least had passed. He had been tested in battle, blooded, thrown into a hectic situation on short notice, and won his spurs, so to speak. All had sent him giant strides forward in a demanding sport where only the fittest survived.

The bus door slammed shut. Ronnie smiled in the gathering darkness, dreaming of Christmas at home, as the vehicle rolled toward the Dallas airport.

Whitman ADVENTURE and MYSTERY Books